ALCOHOLISM

Readers in Social Problems

DONALD R. CRESSEY, CONSULTING EDITOR
UNIVERSITY OF CALIFORNIA, SANTA BARBARA

ALCOHOLISM

EDITED BY

DAVID J. PITTMAN

WASHINGTON UNIVERSITY
ST. LOUIS, MISSOURI

HARPER & ROW

Publishers

NEW YORK, EVANSTON, AND LONDON

Library of Congress Catalog Card Number: 67-12544

TO

RUTH

"a constant bulwark of support"

CONTENTS

vii

PART IV / THE TREATMENT OF ALCOHOLICS: SOME SOCIAL CONSIDERATIONS

PART V / WHAT HAPPENS TO ALCOHOLICS?

PART VI / SOCIAL RESPONSES TO ALCOHOLISM

PREFACE

ALCOHOLISM is viewed as a disease by reputable medical authorities today, but of course there are many social ramifications to this disorder. Alcoholism has not always been perceived as a social and medical problem; as recently as World War II it was conceived of in basically moral terms. In the United States, it is perhaps the most neglected social and medical disorder, and special training for professionals in coping with alcoholism is limited to a few academic centers.

Alcoholism is a multidisciplinary problem which involves researchers and practitioners from the biological and natural sciences, the psychological sciences, and the social sciences. The orientations of these various disciplines, of course, differ in terms of their concepts of alcoholism and the alcoholic. But the constant thread that runs through them is the necessity for further research into the etiology of the disorder and the various means by which it may be treated and eventually brought under control.

This book of readings has been organized into six sections, which represent the variety of disciplines involved. Section 1, "Drinking Patterns and Alcoholism: A Cross-Cultural Perspective," is concerned with a worldwide overview of drinking practices. It is felt that by understanding the "normal" drinking practices that some light might be shed on more pathological forms of drinking behavior. Section 2, concerned with "Physical and Psychosocial Orientations to Alcoholism," brings to the student the experiences of an internist, Dr. Kendis, who has spent more than 25 years in treating alcoholics, and the clinical experience of a psychiatrist, Dr. Catanzaro. In Section 3, "Some Socio-Cultural Aspects of Alcoholism," the concern is with providing systematic research information on the drinking patterns of some specific groups in the society, i.e., teenagers, Negroes, and chronic drunkenness offenders. This section includes an article by the brilliant young attorney, Peter Barton Hutt, whose fights in the court have brought a degree of legal recognition to the statement that "alcoholism is a disease." Section 4, "The Treatment of Alcoholics," reflects a strong social orientation. The two articles here have grown out of the experiences of a multi-disciplinary team, which not only organized the first public treatment facility for alcoholics in Missouri but also established the first detoxification station (in St. Louis) in the western hemisphere. Section 5, "What Happens to Alcoholics," presents one of the most complex areas in this field. All too frequently individuals are given treatment for various disorders, but their long-term progress is un-noted. One of the difficulties which has constantly confronted alcoholism workers has been the invalid assumption that very few alcoholics can be helped and that even fewer can recover. The data presented by Sarah Boggs indicate the fallaciousness of this statement. The last section deals with the "Social Responses to Alcoholism" at the local, community, national, and international levels. It is still one of the few health problems on which the state and local agencies spend far more money than does the federal government. Unfortunately, the interest of the federal establishment in alcoholism has been minimal, and the problem has tended to be swept under the carpet of bureaucratic inertia. In 1966, less than $7 million was expended by the national government on alcoholism research, treatment, and prevention.

Thus, the major purpose of this reader is to present the results from recent scientific studies on alcoholism and clinical experiences of practitioners in this field. We have relied heavily upon materials which were specially prepared instead of excerpting from older and sometimes outdated studies.

The editor would like to acknowledge the extensive support received in preparing this reader from Arline Blodgett, Sarah L. Boggs, Duff G. Gillespie, Joseph B. Kendis, Laura E. Root, Muriel W. Sterne, and Robert L. Tate. In every stage in preparing this reader the diligence and support of my administrative assistant, Ruth Bruce, have been indispensable.

DAVID J. PITTMAN

St. Louis, Missouri

PART I

Drinking Patterns and Alcoholism: A Cross-Cultural Perspective

1

International Overview:
Social and Cultural Factors
in Drinking Patterns,
Pathological and Nonpathological

DAVID J. PITTMAN

INTRODUCTION

Until recently, sociologists, psychologists, psychoanalysts, and economists have largely ignored the importance of drinking practices and behaviors while drinking for understanding the social and cultural context in which drinking pathologies develop. Thus, behavioral scientists are in the same situation as the psychoanalysts and psychiatrists whose almost exclusive concern with neuroses, psychoses, and other mental disorders allows them to make few generalizations about nonpathological behavior. Thus, this article is concerned with an inter-

SUPPORTED (in part) by a Mental Health Project Grant (MH657) from the National Institute of Mental Health, United States Public Health Service.

Parts of this article were presented at the University of Groningen, Groningen, The Netherlands, May, 1963; the Ninth European Institute on the Prevention and Treatment of Alcoholism, Lausanne, Switzerland, June 10–21, 1963; the Workshop for Clergymen, Lake Windermere, Missouri, U.S.A., June 1–3, 1964; the First International Congress on Social Psychiatry, London, England, August 17–22, 1964; the 27*th* International Congress on Alcoholism, Frankfurt am Main, West Germany, September 6–12, 1964; and the Special Conference, "Alcohol and Accidents" at the Department of Health, Education, and Welfare, Washington, D.C., September 17, 1965, sponsored by the Secretary of Health, Education, and Welfare, John W. Gardner.

national overview of drinking practices and the relationship of these drinking practices to sociological variables of age, sex, social class position, and nationality status. This international overview must of necessity be selective since adequate information and analysis exist for only a few societies, whether literate or nonliterate, whether historical or contemporary.

Moreover, each culture reflects a general ethos or sense of decorum about the use and role of alcoholic beverages within its social structure. This ethos may also be conceptualized as the cultural attitudes toward drinking and drunkenness which exist within any society. Suffice it to say that these attitudes run the gamut from absolute prohibition upon ingesting alcoholic beverages to attitudes of permissiveness. Furthermore, social anthropologists have indicated that their theoretical formulations for analyses of drinking behaviors "fall into the categories of 'integrative,' 'anxiety reduction,' or 'disintegrative' with respect to social and psychological functions."[1]

Only by obtaining more knowledge on specific cultural attitudes toward drinking and drunkenness, and the function and role of drinking in diverse culture, will researchers begin to understand and explain pathological drinking. An approach which begins with a concern with drinking practices would allow one to specify those drinking occasions and situations which fall within a culture's permitted range and those which are deviant and may indicate the beginning of a drinking pathology. Moreover, one must constantly ask how drinking practices relate to other institutional structures within the culture, such as religion, economics, and family. This approach would allow one to construct for some cultures the social and dietary norms of drinking which are essential for defining the "excessive" component in the World Health Organization Committee of Experts' definition of alcoholism. Their definition of alcoholism is

Alcoholics are those excessive drinkers whose dependence upon alcohol has attained such a degree that it results in noticeable mental disturbance, or in an interference with their bodily and mental health, their interpersonal relations, their smooth social and economic functioning or those who show the prodromal signs of such developments.[2]

The general areas discussed in this international overview of drinking practices are relevant to any specific culture. The following basic questions are posed for analysis:

1. What are the cultural attitudes toward drinking?
2. How extensive is the use of alcohol beverages within the culture?
3. What social and psychological functions does drinking serve both on the individual and societal level?
4. What is the relationship of drinking practices to the sociological variables of age, sex, and social class position?

CULTURAL ATTITUDES AND DRINKING PRACTICES

All cultures possess a set of attitudes toward the ingestion of alcoholic beverages, and some rigidly define expected and prohibited behaviors while drinking. Theoretically it is possible to range all cultures on a continuum in reference to their attitudes about drinking. At least four cultural positions can be constructed. These are:

1. The cultural attitude is negative and prohibitive toward any type of ingestion of alcoholic beverages. This may be referred to as the *Abstinent Culture.*
2. The cultural attitude toward beverage alcohol usage is one of conflict between co-existing value structures. This may be called the *Ambivalent Culture.*
3. The cultural attitude toward ingesting beverage alcohol is permissive, but negative toward drunkenness and other drinking pathologies. For labeling, we refer to this as the *Permissive Culture.*
4. The cultural attitude is permissive toward drinking, to behaviors which occur when intoxicated, and to drinking pathologies. In one sense, this type, the *Over-Permissive Culture,* does not occur completely in societies, but only approximations in certain nonliterate societies, in those cultures undergoing considerable social change, and those in which there are strong economic vested interests in the production and distribution of alcoholic beverages.

Abstinent Cultures

Numerous cultures have as a basic tenet abstaining from alcoholic beverages. Three broad cultural groupings should be noted—namely, people living in the Islam, Hindu, and Ascetic Protestant traditions.

In Islam Mohammed, the Prophet, proclaimed "The use of spirits was prohibited by the Koran," and historically, the Islamic tradition has been antagonistic toward drinking in North Africa, the Middle East, and India.[3] Furthermore, Mohammed forbade believers to sell or dispense alcoholic beverages. That some Moslems do drink in these areas is reflective of cultural diffusion of European patterns and the decay of tradition as industrialization and urbanization occur.

Both custom and tradition in Hindu Indian society established a moral standard which negatively evaluated the drinking of alcoholic beverages. For example, the Indian lawgiver, Manu, classed beverage alcohol drinking as one of the greatest antisocial acts or sins and suggested abstention.[4] The principle of total abstinence and Prohibition is reflected in the Indian Constitution (Part IV, Article 47), written after independence was achieved from Great Britain. The article in part states:

. . . and in particular, the state shall endeavour to bring about prohibition of consumption, except for medicinal purposes, of intoxicating drinks and drugs which are injurious to health.[4]

Thus, all Indian states are to work toward Prohibition in accord with the Constitutional Provision. Thus far, not all Indian states have complied with this provision.

In Western culture, particularly in Northern and Western Europe and the United States, historically, the emergence of all powerful temperance movements, especially during the nineteenth century and the early part of the twentieth century, has been intimately related to ascetic Protestantism. For example, the first recorded total abstinence pledge in Great Britain was taken by a clergyman, the Reverend Robert Bolton in 1637.[5] In 1809 an Anglican minister, Reverend Cowherd, converted to the Swedenborg Doctrine, made total abstinence a prerequisite for membership in his Bible Christian

Church in Salford, England.[5] His disciples and other temperance leaders in Western culture saw in the drinking of spirits the cause of the social evils concomitant with the Industrial Revolution. These early reform movements, however, were geared toward moderate drinking, and not total abstinence.

In the United States and Great Britain, the total abstinence position captured the temperance movement. In the United States the rise to dominance of the abstinence and Prohibition orientation was intimately related to the ascendance of the middle class, who viewed sobriety as a necessary trait for achievement and success in the emerging capitalistic economic system. Abstinence formed a part of a larger value structure of ascetic Protestantism which was hostile to expressions of emotional impulses. Thus in many Protestant groupings there was a prohibition not only on drinking but upon dancing, use of tobacco, recreation on Sunday, and use of cosmetics.

In part of Northern and Western Europe, however, some temperance movements have concentrated more on what the word temperance actually means, i.e., the use of alcoholic beverages in moderate amounts or the nonusage of spirits with moderate consumption of beer and wines. In the United States, the distinction between temperance and abstinence has been lost, and the terms, unfortunately, are used synonymously.

The emphasis on abstinence and temperance in Western culture must however be viewed as a social movement which attempted to cope with the problems of the Industrial Revolution and concomitant urbanization. In ascetic Protestant beliefs an attempt was made to apply the Christian principles to the everyday world of the workman. In the nineteenth century in England the consumption of spirits increased rapidly and the new factory occupations encouraged drinking among the workmen (Note 5, p. 133). The reformers, in their naive belief that drinking and drunkenness were the keys to social disorganization and personal pathologies of the Industrial Revolution, were relatively unconcerned with the social causes of drunkenness.

The abstinent subcultures are still in existence today in large parts of Finland, Sweden, Norway, Great Britain, Canada, and the United States, and in the religious groups of the Christian Scientists, Mormons, Seventh Day Adventists, Pentecostal Churches, and some Baptists and Methodist religious groups.

Ambivalent Cultures

In cultures, such as in the United States or Ireland marked by ambivalence toward beverage alcohol usage, there is conflict between co-existing value structures. In some non-Western primitive societies or among the American Indians, traditional values are in the process of change or disintegration due to cultural contact with other societies. Examples of societies whose rate of cultural change is so rapid that stable attitudes toward beverage alcohol are disintegrating are found in certain Polynesian societies, studied by Lemert, and the Agringados, Mexican-Americans, found in South Texas, who are rejecting the Mexican-American way of life and have begun to identify with the American culture.[6] Another type of ambivalence as noted by Krauweel in the Netherlands is that some societies, such as the Dutch, accept drinking but reject the drinker who becomes an alcoholic.

Probably in American society one finds the prototype of the ambivalent culture. The American cultural attitudes toward drinking are far from being uniform and "social ambivalence" is reinforced by the conflict between the drinking and abstinent sentiments co-existing in many communities. Strains toward drinking are found in certain religious groups whose ceremonies include the use of alcohol (e.g., Jews), persons who have traditionally regarded the use of liquor as the appropriate means of expressing hospitality and sociability (e.g., Irish-Catholics), and, of course, the liquor industry. Abstinent groups are characteristically composed of ascetic Protestant groups who believe the use of alcohol is sinful and who therefore see little difference between the occasional social drinker and the chronic inebriate, since the former is the beginning stage for the latter.[7]

Drinking pathologies in American society are perpetuated by cultural attitudes that veer toward asceticism and hedonism. Myerson[8] has used the phrase, "social ambivalence," in reference to American cultural attitudes toward drinking. It is his position that this ambivalence limits the development of stable attitudes toward drinking that are found in certain other cultures; moreover, it restricts the meaning of drinking to one of hedonism and insulates drinking practices from social controls. Thus, drinking becomes an extreme and uncontrolled form of behavior for many. Some verification is found for this position in Skolnick's[9] study which finds more alcoholic complications in groups of students from abstinent backgrounds. Skolnick states: "Total abstinence teaching which impounds and implants a repugnance to drinking and inebriety tends to identify the act of drinking with personal and social disorganizations. Thus, it inadvertently suggests an inebriety pattern for drinking and encourages behavior it most deplores."[9]

In this statement Skolnick is suggesting that individuals who become alienated from their abstinence backgrounds may use excessive drinking as a means to act out their frustrations against early family, religious, and community teachings about drinking. In this situation, problem drinking, viewed against a background of total abstinence, becomes a symbol of revolt and attempted escape from early inculcated values.

Another culture with ambivalent attitudes toward drinking is that of the Irish. The Irish male's drinking is dissociated from the network of religious ideas and, furthermore, is not part of the family's usual social routines. Some of the drinking is convivial in nature. As Bales has indicated:

> . . . drinking together is a symbolic . . . manifestation of the solidarity of "friends" or kinship groups, of the acceptance of the individual male as a "man among men," as an equal in his own . . . age group; drinking together is a manifestation of the equality and solidarity of town and country folk, of the guest and host, the politician and his constituents, the seller and the buyer.[10]

But Irish drinking is also utilitarian in the sense that the anesthetic effects of alcohol provide a means of handling psychological tensions. Given the fact that Ireland has the latest age at first marriage for males (around 35 years of age) in the world, drinking by males serves to reduce sexual tensions and familial conflicts.

Permissive Cultures

Permissive cultures are those in which the prevailing attitude is positive toward the use of alcoholic beverages. There may, however, be attitudes as among the Jews which proscribe drunkenness. Examples of permissive cultures are found in Spain, Portugal, Italy, and Japan, and among New York's Chinese and in the Jewish religious group.

Both Snyder and Lolli have reported that Jews and Italians are almost universally exposed to alcoholic beverage usage. One survey,[11] for example, reported that 87 per cent of the Jews were users of alcoholic beverages. But alcoholism rates among the Jewish[12] and Italian[13] ethnic groups are low in comparison to those among Irish[14] and Scandinavian groups.

The crucial fact in explaining low alcoholism pathology among the Jews is based upon more than their permissive attitudes toward drinking. Snyder[12] has indicated in traditional Judaism drinking is integrated into the "traditional rituals of the annual cycle of holy days and festivals, the *rites de passage*, and the observance of Sabbath." Furthermore, drinking is learned in a highly controlled ritualized manner within the family context. Drunkenness is negatively evaluated and sobriety is viewed as a Jewish virtue.

Permissiveness toward use of alcoholic beverages is a characteristic feature of Italian culture where, according to Sadoun and Lolli, such protective features as "early exposure to dilute alcoholic beverages" within the family, parental acceptance of moderate drinking, and the "use of alcohol as a food to be taken in moderation with meals"[15] occur.

Over-Permissive Cultures

As noted before, this is a polar type of cultural attitude which exists only in part, never in entirety. The attitude toward drinking, to behaviors which occur when intoxicated, and to drinking pathologies is permissive.

A partial representation of this cultural attitude is found in Japanese culture.[16] Drinking of *sake*, a rice wine, and beer is widespread, and the act of drinking has many traditional and ritualistic meanings. The traditional attitude of tolerance toward the drinker, reflected in excusing him for his misbehavior as the alcohol is the offender not the drinker, has been partially replaced by a harsher one.

In the Camba society, located in Eastern Bolivia in South America, on festive occasions the population drink a highly concentrated alcoholic beverage, and drunkenness becomes a norm and a part of the social ritual. As Heath has noted:

> Drunkenness is consciously sought as an end in itself, and consensus supports its value. Aggression and sexual license are conspicuously absent on those sole occasions when beverage alcohol is used. Moreover there is no evidence whatsoever of individual instances of dependence upon alcohol comparable to alcoholism or addiction as it is known in the United States.[17]

The problem of classifying the cultural attitude in France is a complex one. There is no doubt about the fact that the attitude toward drinking is highly permissive. One attitude survey of French people, although somewhat outdated by a 1953 publication date, reported that for a man doing physical work, 25 percent of the sample felt wine was indispensable, 63 percent classified wine as useful, 70 percent felt wine was nourishing and 80 percent felt wine was good for the health.[18]

Furthermore, France has the highest per capita rate of alcohol consumption in the world, and "in Europe, the highest rates of alcohol addiction and deaths due to alcoholic cirrhosis of the liver" (Note 15, p. 449).

In a lecture at the 1963 European Institute on Alcoholism at Lausanne, Professor Fouquet has provided an excellent analysis of the French problem with an emphasis upon the economic factors. What role does the production of alcohol and spatial distribution of its production and consumption have on the genesis of alcoholism? These factors have largely been ignored by Americans. In France, Fouquet reports that at least three and one-half million people are engaged in viticulture and the production and distribution of alcoholic beverages.[19] Fouquet supports his contention that there is a relationship between the economic factor of production, alcoholization, and alcoholism by referring to the noted French study of Ledermann, Trevas and Hong,[19] which shows that the commitments for alcoholic psychoses vary directly with density of home production of alcoholic beverages or the importance of wine-growing. From this classic study we can infer that the French population is permissive not only towards alcohol beverage production but also to the pathologies that develop from excessive ingestion of alcohol.

EXTENSIVENESS OF ALCOHOL BEVERAGE USAGE

Regardless of whether the culture is an abstinent one, a certain amount of drinking occurs, and conversely in the permissive culture a group of abstainers will exist. Thus, although extensiveness of beverage usage correlates with cultural type, it is not a perfect correlation. More specifically, in Hindu culture, an abstinent one, in most of the exterior castes, like "khatiks," "Bhangis," and "Lodhs," the use of alcohol by both men and women is approved, and the children begin to drink at an early age.[20] Drinking pathologies are found, for example, in Lucknow, India, a wet area, which resemble the Western type of alcoholism. In speaking of inebriate parents who are dipsomaniacs, Srisastaua states:

> They [the dipsomaniacs] lose their balance of mind, after a heavy intake and become most irrational in behavior. Invariably in these cases ordinary family obligations are neglected and children particularly are ill treated (note 20, p. 69).

In The Netherlands, an ambivalent culture towards drinking, an excellent study of drinking and smoking habits was conducted on a random sample of the Dutch population in 1958 by the eminent sociologist, Professor Ivan Gadourek.[21] The percentage of abstainers in the adult population is from 15 to 21 percent; for that 80 percent of the population which drinks, it does not occur at meals as in Italy. Much the same situation is found in survey results from the State of California in the United States; in the adult sample only 13 percent were abstainers while the remainder were users.[22]

The extreme of the drinking culture is perhaps found in France where only 4 percent of the native French population are abstainers.[19] A recent Polish survey on a representative survey of the population 20 years of age and over found 15.7 percent abstainers, with the percentage 25.1 percent among women and 7.6 percent among men.[23] Also, few teetotallers would be found in Italy and among the Jews.

Furthermore, the type and amount of beverage alcohol consumed varies from one cultural type to another. In a characterization of beverage preferences McDouall has stated:

> Before the war [Second World War] the French drank champagne, Spaniards drank sherry, Portuguese port; Germans drank beer, Italians chianti, Scandinavians *schnapps;* and the Russians drank—and still drink—vodka. In Balkan countries they drank plum brandy calling it *slivovicz* in Yugoslavia, *tswika* in Rumania and other things elsewhere; Greeks drank *retsina*, Turks *arak*. West Indians drank rum. Americans drank cocktails, highballs and iced water.[24]

We doubt whether drinking preferences have changed as radically as McDouall maintains in his article. But changes in preference and consumption patterns have occurred. For example, in 1961 the estimated consumption of whiskey in France was 682,000 gallons which represented a doubling of the 1960 consumption, although much of the whiskey was used for cooking purposes.[25] In Italy even more dramatic changes in consumption patterns have occurred. In the 20-year period from 1941–1961 there has been a 100-percent increase in the consumption of wine; beer consumption has increased by 200 percent and spirits by 400 percent.[26]

SOCIETAL AND INDIVIDUAL FUNCTIONS OF DRINKING

The ingestion of alcoholic beverages in each culture carries with it social psychological functions and meanings. At least two basic ways of classifying the functions of drinking have been suggested. One scheme suggested by social anthropologists and sociologists who adhere to the "Functional School" is to categorize drinking practices as being (1) integrative for the individual and the social system; (2) anxiety-reducing, particularly for the individual; and (3) disintegrative for the social system and the individual.[1]

A scheme more preferred by this writer is the one advanced by Bales who has suggested that alcoholic beverages can serve one or more of the following functions for cultural groups. Those functions are: (1) religious, (2) ceremonial, (3) hedonistic, and (4) utilitarian (Note 10, pp. 183–185). Religious functions of alcoholic beverages are numerous. Only mentioned here will be the use of wine to be consecrated for Holy Communion in Roman Catholicism and in some Protestant groups.

Ceremonial usages of alcoholic beverages may be found in connection with many of the major *rites de passage* from birth to death in Western society. Some illustrations can be provided such as the drinking of wine at the Jewish boy's *Bar Mitzvah*, the wedding celebration with champagne in the middle classes of America, and the drinking of whiskey by the Irish at wakes.

Hedonistic or pleasurable usages of alcoholic beverages are also well documented. One form is basically convivial in which the individual drinks with another or a group to show his solidarity with friends and kinship groups.[10] Also one may obtain the pleasurable psychological effects of a generally euphoric feeling. This takes linguistic expression in the English language in the phrases—"to get high" or "to have a glow on."[27] In the case of many Western alcoholics, however, what began as a pleasurable activity becomes a burdensome addiction after a period of years.

Utilitarian drinking refers to using alcohol to gain some "relief or satisfaction of self-oriented, self-contained needs" or "gain some personal advantage over the other" (Note 10, p.184). One notable utilitarian function of alcoholic beverages in Western culture is the use for medicinal purposes. Even during Prohibition in American society alcohol could be obtained on a physician's prescription. In Irish culture, studied by Bales, beverage alcohol was used for a variety of ills, such as colds, diarrhea, cholera, and fevers. In his words:

> Its [alcohol] everyday use to begin the day, to get rid of a "hangover," to quiet hunger, to relieve stomach disorder, to get warm, to keep warm, to reward the child, to release sexual and aggressive tensions, to relieve emotional difficulties ranging from minor upsets and disappointments to deep grief, to restore consciousness in case of fainting and shock, to improve the physician's skill, to dispel fatigue and to promote sleep—all of these and more are utilitarian uses . . . (Note 10, p. 185).

Utilitarian functions of beverage alcohol can be found in most cultures, especially medicinal ones and occasionally against legal prohibitions. In Czechoslovakia, despite legal regulations which prohibit the giving by parents of beverage alcohol to children under 18, parents use alcohol as a medicine against such things as tooth and stomach aches.[28]

Harold Pfautz, the American sociologist, has studied the functions of alcoholic beverages in an interesting way. His study was based on a content analysis of selected "best-seller" novels for two distinct time periods, 1900–1904, and 1946–1950. His aim was to classify the functions attributed to beverage alcohol. By far the most frequently noted one was the support of social relationships. Other functions discerned were medical support of the individual, cooking, psychic support of the individual, and ritual. Two major types of dysfunctions were noted—namely, destruction of social relationships and physical and mental harm to the individual.[29]

In conclusion, it should be stated that the functions performed by alcohol in one culture are related to the whole cultural system and find meaning within that context.

DRINKING PRACTICES: THEIR RELATION TO AGE AND SEX AND STRATIFICATION SYSTEMS

Age and sex status and position in the stratification system are three important variables which all societies use in defining expected behaviors and role performances of their members. They are also related within a society to expected drinking practices and behaviors.

Age

Age grading has been noticed in all human societies. Simply stated, expected behaviors change as the individual moves from childhood to adolescence to maturity to old age. How then is age related to drinking behavior?

A cross-cultural examination shows wide variation in reference to the age at which the individual is allowed access to beverage alcohol. At one extreme are the cases of Italy and France in which the child is at an early age introduced to drinking through his family. The family provides beverage alcohol, especially wine, at meals and for medicinal purposes. Sometimes the child receives too much wine, becomes intoxicated, and requires medical attention. Thus it is no accident that one center for the study of alcoholism in Italy is located within the Gaslini Pediatrics Institute at the University of Genoa. At Genoa, Professor Dalla Volta has concentrated on the study of child "alcoholism" and its relation to adult alcoholism, as well as an examination of the geographic areas where child alcoholism is high.[30] In France, educational campaigns under the High Committee of Study and Information on Alcoholism have urged parents not to give wine to the children. The same position has been taken by the Health Ministries in Czechoslovakia and Hungary for example. Thus in one group of countries children are introduced to beverage alcohol in their homes by their parents at an early age. However, as the cases of France and Czechoslovakia indicate, this practice does not immunize the child against alcoholism as some American observers have naively assumed.

At the other extreme of the continuum is American society in which almost all states prohibit complete access to the purchase and consumption of all types of alcoholic beverages until the legal age of 21. Participation in the drinking subculture occurs before this—in adolescence between ages

16–18. Maddox,[31] from his analysis of studies in America concerned with adolescent drinking, indicates that the drinking practices of youth are highly predictable from the drinking patterns of their parents and that first drinking experiences tend to occur in the home under parental supervision.

Social ambivalence, of course, is indicated in the contradiction between the legal age of 21, when drinking is allowed without restriction, and the earlier introduction into drinking by parents and friends. In late adolescence and early youth (ages 18–21) drinking behavior and expectancies are poorly defined and social control mechanisms are circumvented by the youth. Thus, the stage is set for the development of alcoholic pathologies.

Sex

One of the most important variables governing drinking is that of sex status. Unfortunately drinking practices by sex have hardly been studied. Despite this, most surveys do contain some information on drinking status and frequency. For example, the Dutch sample survey previously cited[21] indicates that sex is among the major causes of variation in drinking habits. In comparison to men, women drink more at home, excessive and habitual drinking is infrequent, and craving for alcohol is rare. In the Polish survey by Swiecicki, in the rural area men drank 5.6 times as much intoxicating beverages as women while in urban areas the men were drinking four times as much as the women.[23]

Surveys on the frequency and the amount of drinking in the United States indicate that fewer females than males drink and that when they do drink females consume less than males. This difference is further reflected in the fact that in the United States there are four to five times as many male alcoholics as female ones.

The facts that in Western cultures fewer women become drinkers than men, and that the female drinks less than her male counterpart set the stage on which there will be fewer female alcoholics. Therefore, we should view the claims of such observers as Marvin Block[32] and Ruth Fox, that there are as many American female as male alcoholics, as being without foundation.

Stratification Systems

All societies are divided into major status divisions, based upon such factors as income, occupation, education, or other attributes highly valued by the society. These classes have differential access to rewards and privileges within the society. We can attempt to analyze and understand a society's drinking practices in terms of its stratification and occupational systems. As yet these investigations are limited, and we will confine ourselves to only a few in this article.

American sociologists have frequently examined drinking practices by social class and have found them to vary. The pioneer work was completed by John Dollard[33] over two decades ago who pointed out that for the upper class, and this would be true for the middle class as well today, anti-social behavior while drinking is forbidden; moreover, aggressive behavior in the guise of verbal insult is frowned upon. It is within the most marginal economic classes in America that one finds the concentration of intoxication-related problems dealing with the control of aggression. In these classes the norms controlling expectancies and behavior while drinking are ill-defined. Much drinking is without restraint, and frequently participants engage in violent aggressive behavior or choose socially inappropriate public places to become intoxicated.

The cosmopolitanism of the new middle classes in American society today supports the norm of permissive drinking, and abstinence has become a negative symbol of life style. As one American temperance writer has indicated, "Cocktails or scotch and soda have become a badge of membership in the upper middle class to which every college student aspires."[34] Thus, in American middle classes currently there is an emphasis upon drinking. To drink is to be a cosmopolitan and carries with it the implication of emancipation from traditional American values.

In that American invention, the cocktail party, one finds the best reflection of current drinking expectancies and practices in the upper and middle classes. On the descriptive level, the cocktail party is the gathering together of a mixed age, sex, and, at times, social class collectivity at which no planned activity occurs. The host or hostess performs his function in most respects prior to the onset of the party by assembling the guest list and providing both physical locale and alcoholic beverages; these are sometimes supplemented by limited food. As David Riesman[35] has so cogently indicated, the cocktail party has a "vanishing host," i.e., the party can continue without the presence of the host. Participants in the party arrive, secure drinks, and engage in aimless conversation while standing. The plight of the abstainer and the abstinent alcoholic is sometimes vividly portrayed in the absence of any nonalcoholic beverage at the party.

Behavioral scientists have also begun studies on occupational groups to determine the relationship between the work position and drinking behavior. Theoretically the assumption is that certain personality types are selected for specific occupations and that changes occur in the personality while the individual is being socialized to the occupation.

In reference to drinking behavior it is assumed that certain occupations, such as merchant seamen or house painters, recruit and socialize men to a heavy drinking subculture. One occupational group which has been studied from this point of view is that of merchant seamen, but results from Sweden and Italy are contradictory.

Swedish studies show that chronic alcoholism among seafarers is common. One specific study[36] involved the analysis of all seafarers registered in Sweden dying in 1945–1954, of whom 1775 were Swedish and 236 were foreign. Of the Swedish group, 3.6 percent were alcohol addicts when they first signed on, their median length of service was 22.3 years, but 18.3 percent were chronic alcoholics when they last signed on. Thus, a significant number became addicts after becoming seamen. Furthermore, among those who died in the Swedish alcohol addict group, 41.1 percent committed suicide, an extremely high number.

An Italian study by Bonfiglio and Cicala[37] on alcoholism among Italian seamen reports contradictory results from the Swedish one. They made personal inquiries on Italian merchant ships in the seaports of Civitavecchia (seaport near Rome) and Naples, and sent a questionnaire to several captains of Italian merchant ships; furthermore, they interviewed the physicians of the "Casse Mutue Marittime" (association dealing with maritime problems) and of hospitals in Civitavecchia and Naples, police authorities in the said cities, and some ship's doctors; finally they studied the incidence of seamen among the alcoholic psychotics in the psychiatric hospitals of Rome and Genoa.

From these data it appears that alcoholism is practically non-existent among Italian seamen and that the rate of alcoholism in this occupational group is lower than in other groups. To explain this, the authors advanced hypotheses founded primarily on the socio-economic conditions which allow navigation companies to be highly selective in their hiring process. In short, they feel that potential alcoholics have been screened out, but we would not rule out the importance of Swedish and Italian normative orientations to drinking which are quite different—namely, the ambivalent culture in Sweden, and the permissive one in Italy.

SUMMARY

Sociological research into drinking practices and their relationship to the larger sociocultural organization has just begun. On an applied level, a knowledge of the meaning and functions which groups attribute to drinking is essential if social policy is to be formulated and programs to combat drinking pathologies are to be instituted.

PART II

Physical
and Psychosocial
Orientations
to Alcoholism

2

The Human Body and Alcohol

JOSEPH B. KENDIS

In this article we will discuss the physiology and metabolism of alcohol. First of all let us consider, what is alcohol? It is a chemical compound composed of varying parts of carbon, hydrogen, and oxygen. The number of parts of each of these chemical elements in this compound determines which one of the numerous alcohols it might be. In certain combinations these elements will join to form methyl alcohol, the one commonly used in paint thinner or as an antifreeze in automobile radiators. Other combinations will give us ethyl alcohol, propyl alcohol, isopropyl alcohol, amyl alcohol (which is known also as fusel oil and is found in small amounts in most distilled beverages), or numerous other alcohols. However, the one alcohol that is used in alcoholic beverages is ethyl alcohol. The formula for ethyl alcohol is written as C_2H_5OH. This denotes that this compound has in it two molecules of carbon connected with five molecules of hydrogen, and this in turn connected with one molecule each of oxygen and hydrogen. Ethyl alcohol is a clear, colorless liquid, rather volatile and with a strong burning taste and very little odor; however, the odor on one's breath after imbibing alcoholic beverages is due more to other things in the beverage than to the alcohol. Ethyl alcohol is the one used mostly for alcoholic beverages for several reasons. First, it is easy to produce by fermentation. Although all alcohols are toxic or poisonous in varying degrees to the body, ethyl alcohol seems to have somewhat lower toxicity than many of the others. Second, it has what many people describe as a pleasant taste, and finally, it can be made quite easily in a concentrated form by distillation.

It was mentioned that all alcohols exert toxic effects on the body, and when ingested the degree of toxicity or intoxication is dependent on the amount of alcohol that is found in the various body cells. This in turn, of course, is dependent on how rapidly the body can break down, burn, or oxidize the particular alcohol. One of the factors which makes ethyl alcohol best suited for consumption in alcoholic beverages is its rapidity of oxidation by the body. An average-sized man will oxidize about three-fourths of an ounce to one ounce of whiskey per hour.

In this article when we discuss alcohol, we will be speaking of ethyl alcohol, because this is, as has been said, the one that is most commonly used in alcoholic beverages. The amount of alcohol in various alcoholic beverages varies greatly from about 4 percent up to as high as about 50 percent. In beverages of lower alcoholic concentrations, such as the beers and the wines, the strength of alcohol is usually expressed in percentages. Most beers, for instance, have about 4 percent alcohol and wines from about 12 to 16 percent alcohol. In the distilled beverages, however, the strength of the alcohol is not expressed in percentage but in proof. The term *proof* when speaking of the strength of alcohol in a beverage, goes back to the early days of distillation when the purchaser would mix some of the beverage with gunpowder and then apply a match to it. If it burned, this was proof of the alcoholic content. Over a period of time, however, numerical values were given, so that the strength of a distilled beverage was then expressed as a number. If one were able to manufacture and preserve pure alcohol, it would be spoken of as being two hundred proof. However, pure alcohol has such an affinity for water that it will dilute itself from the moisture in the air about it. The strongest alcohol we can usually find will measure about one hundred eighty proof. Most distilled alcoholic beverages will be of a strength of about eighty-five to one hundred proof (about 50 percent, a little more or less).

Thus we can describe alcoholic beverages as follows:

(a) The brewed beverages or beers which usually measure about 4 percent alcohol

(b) The fermented beverages or wines usually measuring from 12 to 16 percent alcohol
(c) The distilled beverages usually about 50 percent alcohol (eighty-five to one hundred proof)

The brewed beverages or beers are made by fermentation of grains, the wines by fermentation of fruits, and the distilled beverages by distilling beer or wine (distilling grain beverages gives whiskey, and distilling fruit beverages gives brandy). There are also other alcoholic beverages such as vodka, which is usually distilled from fermented potatoes in its country of origin, Russia, and gin, which is diluted alcohol with juniper berry flavor added.

Alcohol does not have to be digested, as do some foodstuffs when they are taken into the body, but exerts its action upon the body in its original state. However, in one sense alcohol can be considered a food like other foodstuffs; when it is oxidized or burned in the body, it gives off calories of heat and energy, but it is not a good food. First of all, it cannot be stored by the body as can other foods, and secondly, as it is taken in by the body it exerts its toxic or deleterious effects upon the body. A calorie is a measure of heat when something is burned or oxidized. The calories given off in oxidation of alcohol (about seven calories per gram) are about half way between those given off by the carbohydrates or proteins (about four and one-half calories per gram) and the fats (about nine calories per gram).

When first taken into the mouth and swallowed, alcohol imparts a tingling and somewhat burning sensation to the tongue and throat. This may be one of the reasons some people have the false impression that it is a stimulant. Next, when it reaches the stomach, its action on this organ depends on its strength. Any alcohol over about 4 percent in strength will cause irritation of the delicate membranes of the stomach, and the stomach will quickly secrete digestive juices to dilute the alcohol down to a less irritating strength. In the meantime, the pylorus, a strong ring of muscles at the lower end of the stomach, will tighten and prevent the alcohol from entering the upper portion of the intestine prior to its dilution. If there is enough irritation, there may even be reverse waves in the stomach causing vomiting. Of course, anyone who is so sensitive to alcohol that he would regurgitate before it could exert its action would be unlikely to become an alcoholic.

There are other things, also, which vary the time taken for the alcohol to pass from the stomach to the intestine. If the alcohol were mixed with food, it would, of course, be passed through into the intestine more slowly, as there would be some delay due to partial digestion of the food in the stomach. Carbohydrates (starches and sugars) would slow down the emptying time of the stomach the least and proteins and fats the most. Of course, the alcohol would pass most rapidly through an empty stomach. If someone had not eaten for some time before drinking, he would tend to feel the effects of the alcohol more rapidly. It has even been said that the rapidity of the transmission of foodstuff from the stomach may be varied by one's mood, the mood affecting the autonomic nervous system, which in turn controls the pyloric ring causing it to open or tighten down more. Up to this time little or no alcohol has been absorbed into the blood stream, but once it is passed into the first portion of the small intestine (the duodenum) it is rapidly absorbed through the wall of the intestine into the blood stream and then carried to the various organs of the body. A very small amount of alcohol is picked up by the kidneys and excreted in the urine, a small amount passes through the lungs and is exhaled in the breath, but most of the alcohol is burned or oxidized by the body, almost all of this taking place in the liver, which breaks the alcohol down through a series of stages into carbon dioxide and water. The carbon dioxide is exhaled by the lungs and the water excreted by the kidneys in the urine. The main stages in this process are:

$$\text{alcohol} \rightarrow \text{acetaldehyde} \rightarrow \text{acetic acid} \underset{\rightarrow}{\overset{\rightarrow}{}} \begin{matrix} \text{carbon dioxide} \\ \text{water.} \end{matrix}$$

It is during this oxidation process that energy in the form of heat is given off. This is carried on at a standard rate by all people, as is their metabolism in general. This we can observe, because, knowing that metabolism produces heat, we find the body temperature the same in all healthy individuals. Now, as was previously stated, metabolism of alcohol occurs at about the rate of three-fourths of an ounce to one ounce of whiskey per hour. In other words, if a person were to consume even as much as eighteen ounces of whiskey gradually over a twenty-four hour period (three-fourths of one ounce per hour), he would oxidize the alcohol in the whiskey at the above standard rate of about three-fourths of an ounce to one ounce per hour, so that at no time during the entire twenty-four hours would he experience any effect whatsoever from the alcohol and at no time during that period would we find any alcohol in his blood or tissues, even though he had consumed this large amount of whiskey. The reason, of course, is obvious. His body would be burning or oxidizing the alcohol as fast as it was being ingested. On the same basis, however, if he took even one-half or even one-fourth of this amount of whiskey say, in one hour, we could if we tested at that time find a fairly high concentration of alcohol in his system.

For many years scientists working in the field of alcoholism have attempted to find methods of increasing the rate of oxidation of alcohol by the body, so that one could more quickly rid oneself of the effects of alcohol and alcohol intoxication. Attempts have been made by many modalities, as for instance stimulants such as caffeine in coffee, sudden cold as in cold showers, use of injections of insulin, and the use of thyroid or thyroid-like substances, but most are agreed that none of these attempts or others will change the body's rate of oxidation of alcohol. For instance, running and increasing the need for oxidation of foodstuffs will not cause the alcohol to burn any more rapidly nor will coffee or stimulant or other drugs.

Some of the alcohol not immediately oxidized travels through the body in the blood stream and exerts its toxic effect on the various body organs; the most important ones affected are the brain and central nervous system. Alcohol may have a direct effect on various parts of the body, but this effect is compounded many times by the loss of control over this part of the body due to the effect of alcohol on the brain and central nervous system. One might comparatively think of a telephone exchange operating normally and then having something happen which makes part of it inoperable, so that certain phones do not send out or receive messages or perhaps have a short circuit so that the messages would come through poorly due to changes in sound or volume.

Many people speak of alcohol being a stimulant, but nothing is further from the truth; alcohol has been proved not to be a stimulant but a depressant, but in spite of this some people insist that a drink gives them a lift. However, let us remember many people use alcoholic beverages to relax or as a nightcap to aid sleep, and it is not logical to consider the same chemical acting as a stimulant at one time, a depressant at another. The reasons some people consider alcohol as a stimulant, even though it is not, are that it causes a tingling of the tongue and a slight burning on being swallowed; also, on being absorbed it releases some of the inhibitions normally used to control their lives. Thus they will do things that they might not ordinarily do.

The more lasting effects of alcohol upon the various organs of the body do not appear early in the course of drinking but do show up after a person has continued heavy drinking, either intermittently or continuously over a long period of time (usually somewhere between five and twenty-five years). Dr. R. Gordon Bell of Toronto, Canada, an outstanding figure in the field of alcoholism, has made a movie called, "For Those Who Drink." According to Dr. Bell in the movie, those systems that are most noticeably affected by long continued use of alcohol are the digestive and the nervous systems. The digestive system, of course, reveals such drinking-related changes as gastritis and inflammatory changes of the stomach, and liver changes which eventually become cirrhosis of the liver. Cirrhosis here is considered to be a disease of malnutrition due to drinking while not eating properly over long periods of time. In the beginning there is just swelling and fat being laid down in the liver causing it to increase in size, and later in the course of the disease, the fat is absorbed and replaced by scar tissue, which then starts shrinking; during this time it may shrink to a point where it will squeeze down and either diminish or stop completely the circulation of the blood in the liver or the passage of bile through the various tubules, termed bile ducts. The pancreas may become acutely inflamed causing excruciating pain. The greatest changes shown, however, are those found in the nervous system. These vary from the neuritis which is found in some of the distal nerves (peripheral polyneuritis) usually said to be caused by a lack of vitamin B_1 in the sheath or insulation surrounding each of these nerves to those changes seen in the brain which cause lapses of memory (blackouts), hallucinations, and extreme tremor, as seen in delirium tremens (commonly known as DT's), usually found when an individual who has been drinking heavily over a long period of time attempts to stop drinking. In other cases even more severe changes in the brain and central nervous system will be noted which are of a permanent nature (generally referred to as chronic brain syndrome). Some other effects of alcohol, besides those on the brain and central nervous system, are upon the pituitary gland which ordinarily secretes a substance known as an antidiuretic element. This material ordinarily slows down the flow of urine from the kidneys. However, in the presence of alcohol the action of this gland is reduced and there is usually an increased flow of urine. There is some varying degree of effect of alcohol on all parts of the human body.

The body consists of many chemicals, the one found in the largest amount (approximately 70 percent) being water. Therefore, if one knows how much alcohol a person consumed and his weight, one could closely approximate the amount of alcohol in his tissues. In reverse, also, if we knew his weight and the amount of alcohol in his tissues, we could then tell about how much he had had to drink. This is the basis for the various measuring devices used by the police to tell how much alcohol is in a person's blood or tissues. Of the water in the body, about one-third of it is outside of the body cells and about two-thirds inside. The amount of water outside the cells is usually quite constant, but that inside the cells is quite variable. It will increase after fluid intake and decrease after urination. When a person has had too much to drink and is intoxicated, the total water in the body does not vary especially, but the water does shift from the intracellular to the extracellular state. That is to say, when one becomes intoxicated, there is more water outside of the body cells and less inside. This is why at such a time one feels thirsty. However, as was stated, the most important action of alcohol is that on the brain and central nervous system where it acts as an anesthetic.

To illustrate the effects of alcohol on the brain let us consider that behavior such as judgment and inhibitions begins to be affected even after one drink (causing a concentration of 0.02 percent of alcohol in the blood). If one takes three drinks, causing a concentration of 0.06 percent of alcohol in the blood, reaction time and coordination are affected; five drinks (0.10 percent of alcohol in the blood), vision, speech, and balance start to become affected; and with eight drinks (0.16 percent of alcohol in the blood) the person has trouble walking or standing. After 20 drinks (0.40 percent of alcohol in the blood), consciousness usually goes, and finally if one is able to consume 25 drinks (0.50 percent of alcohol in the blood) death ensues. Of course, one must take into consideration the size of the individual and how rapidly the drinks were consumed, as alcohol oxidation will be going on constantly while drinking occurs.

Thus we see that alcohol exerts its action upon many different parts of the body including the stomach, intestines, liver, pancreas, and pituitary gland among others. All of these effects may then be compounded and made more severe by the loss of control of the various parts of the body due to the anesthetic action of the alcohol upon the brain and central nervous system, which is the controlling mechanism of the body.

3

Psychiatric Aspects of Alcoholism

RONALD J. CATANZARO

Alcoholism is an extremely complex illness which involves psychiatric, physical, sociologic, and cultural areas. An undistorted discussion of the psychiatric aspects of alcoholism can only be accomplished if one keeps in mind that the other three areas mentioned above play an integral part in the psychiatric phenomena observed.

From a psychiatric point of view, an American alcoholic can be defined as a person who has become dependent on the drug, alcohol, consequently drinking more alcohol than those in the culture where he lives, and whose drinking causes problems with his health, home, jobs, and friends. The reader should notice that the above definition applies mainly to alcoholics who live in the United States and, as will be described below, does not describe all alcoholics in all countries.

CLASSIFICATION OF ALCOHOLICS

In order to more fully understand the American alcoholic, it is worthwhile to briefly review the classification of alcoholics as originally proposed by Dr. E. M. Jellinek.[1] He separates alcoholics into four main classifications:

Alpha Alcoholism

Represents a purely psychological continued dependence upon the effect of alcohol to relieve bodily or emotional pain. The drinker violates the rules of society by drinking at unacceptable places and times, imbibing excessive amounts and showing unacceptable behavior while drinking. This type is not characterized though, by loss of control or inability to abstain from drinking, nor are there any signs of a progressive process. The relief of bodily pain or emotional disturbances implies an underlying illness but this species of alcoholism cannot be regarded as an illness in and of itself, according to Jellinek. This is similar to what other authors call symptomatic alcoholism.

Beta Alcoholism

The species of alcoholism in which such alcoholic complications as polyneuropathy, gastritis, and cirrhosis of the liver may occur without either physical or psychological dependence upon alcohol. The incentive to a heavy drinking pattern which leads to such serious complications may be the custom of certain social groups in conjunction with poor nutritional habits. Beta alcoholism is neither a disease *per se* nor a symptom, although the excessive drinking may result in a number of medical illnesses as well as other serious nutritional diseases.

Gamma Alcoholism

The species of alcoholism characterized by (1) acquired increased tissue tolerance to alcohol, (2) adaptive cell metabolism, (3) withdrawal symptoms and "craving," i.e., physical dependence, and (4) loss of control over the use of alcohol. There is a definite progression from psychological to physical dependence and a marked deterioration of behavior. Under certain conditions a person with Alpha or Beta alcoholism may develop into one with Gamma alcoholism. This species produces the most serious kind of damage and is a prevalent type in the United States. This type of alcoholism constitutes a disease in and of itself.

Delta Alcoholism

Shows the same characteristics as Gamma alcoholism except instead of a loss of ability to control the use of alcohol, there is inability to abstain from drinking. Thus the ability to control the amount of intake on any given occasion remains. But if this type of alcoholic stops drinking for even a day or two he experiences a rapid onset of withdrawal symptoms such as tremors and delirium tremens. This type of alcoholic is the most prevalent type in France where cultural values provide a strong incentive to high alcohol intake, mostly of wine. This species of alcoholism is also a disease in and of itself.

In one of Dr. Jellinek's last published articles before his death[2] in 1962, he further defined his classification of American alcoholics as belonging to two main groups: (1) addictive alcoholics, i.e., those who show the progressive signs of deterioration commonly associated with alcoholism and also characterized by loss of control over the use of alcohol; and (2) nonaddictive alcoholics, i.e., those who may show the progressive signs of deterioration of alcoholism but who do not manifest overt loss of control over the use of alcohol.

His description of the addictive alcoholic is essentially identical to his description of the Gamma alcoholic, the major type in the United States. But his description of the nonaddictive alcoholic appears to be a combination of the Alpha and Delta classifications. Like Alpha alcoholics, the nonaddictive alcoholics drink largely to relieve emotional or bodily pain and run into trouble with society because of their drinking pattern, but they do not manifest loss of control over the use of alcohol such as Gamma alcoholics do. However, like Delta alcoholics, nonaddictive alcoholics usually show progressive deterioration and manifest an inability to abstain from the use of alcohol, although this appears to stem from psychological dependence on alcohol rather than a physical dependence on it.

This separation of alcoholics into addictive and nonaddictive types appears to have definite clinical value. For example, this writer's study of compulsory treatment of alcoholic prisoners at a Federal penitentiary in Texas[3] indicated that there appeared to be a difference in these two groups in their response to treatment. The addictive alcoholics were much more responsive to the treatment techniques used than were the nonaddictive ones. Alcoholics Anonymous groups appear to be made up primarily of addictive alcoholics, indicating that the approach to recovery which this group practices may be more helpful to the addictive than the nonaddictive alcoholic. Nonaddictive alcoholics may possibly be better helped by psychologically oriented treatment such as is present in many State Alcoholism Programs and private psychiatric hospitals.

Therefore, alcoholics in the United States consist of two main groups: (1) the nonaddictive alcoholic and (2) the addictive alcoholic. This classification will be further clarified during the subsequent review of the phases of development of alcoholism.

THEORIES CONCERNING THE CAUSES OF ALCOHOLISM

All of the factors involved in a person's developing alcoholism are not yet known. However, a number of theories of etiology are prevalent and each has empirical observations to partially substantiate it. These theories fall into three main categories, i.e., biologic, psychologic, and socio-cultural theories.

1. Biologic Theories

Inherited peculiarities of the organism have been indicted as the cause of alcoholism by many. Dr. E. M. Jellinek, a distinguished scholar in the field of alcoholism, compiled a number of studies dealing with rates of alcoholism in families. He found an over-all average of 52 percent of alcoholics had at least one alcoholic parent. Conversely, the expectancy rate of alcoholism in the children of families where at least one parent is an alcoholic is between 20 and 30 percent. In contrast, the expectancy rate of alcoholism in the general population is only between 2 and 3 percent. This *might mean* that a tendency to develop alcoholism is inherited.

Two additional personal observations have always struck

me as very interesting. First, some of my alcoholic patients have stated that they literally lost control of the use of alcohol with their first experience with alcohol as a youngster. As one alcoholic told me: "The first time I remember drinking was when I was 14 down in my daddy's wine cellar. I drank until I got so drunk and sick I vomited." Many never touched a drink again until years later, and when they did, they again drank to the point of drunkenness and have continued to do so since. One might postulate that these people have a high degree of genetic biological determinancy for addiction to alcohol.

The second interesting observation stems from a group of my patients who are overly dependent, immature, emotionally unstable, come from broken or unhappy homes, and in general have most of the characteristics frequently thought to be the basis of alcoholism by those who adhere to psychologic factors as the cause. Several of these people have told me how they actually set out to become alcoholics during a very unhappy period in their lives. They hoped that once they became alcoholics they wouldn't care about anything anymore, including their troubles. They reported drinking heavily over many months and finally decided the whole experiment was a failure; they didn't get much of a lift out of drinking and were tired of the hangover effects of alcohol, so they quit without any trouble. Some of them stated they take occasional social drinks now and have no desire to drink heavily. One might postulate that these people have a very low degree of genetic biologic determinancy to become addicted to alcohol—"they just don't have what it takes."

Exactly how would such a genetic biologic factor work? R. J. Williams postulates that alcoholism may be caused by an inherited metabolic pattern which results in nutritional deficiencies and consequently gives rise to a craving for the specific nutrient called alcohol. No such metabolic deficiency has been proven. Does the alcoholic suffer from some other type of metabolic abnormality such as an endocrine imbalance, which biologically predisposes him to become addicted to alcohol as J. J. Smith[4] postulates? Again, no conclusive evidence of this has yet to come to light. Could the alcoholic genetically inherit an emotional makeup which predisposes to alcoholism? A fascinating idea, but no convincing evidence exists to support this hypothesis. Others that hold to biologic etiology of alcoholism state that if the biologic factor is not inherited, it may well be acquired. Through repeated bouts of heavy drinking, a person may develop an unusual sensitivity to alcohol. That is, he may actually become allergic to alcohol, as many members of Alcoholics Anonymous believe. Again, no such allergy has ever been demonstrated.

An interesting study was done by M. Freile Fleetwood[5] who measured three chemical substances in the blood of alcoholics as against nonalcoholic controls. One of these substances appeared mostly when a person was anxious (norepinephrine), another when he was tense (acetyl-choline) and a third substance when he was resentful (unidentified substance). He then administered alcohol to the alcoholics and the nonalcoholic controls and remeasured the substances. The only striking difference between the alcoholics and nonalcoholics was that alcohol caused a great reduction in the "resentment substance" in the blood of alcoholics. This would lend some further substance to the idea that there are real biochemical differences between alcoholics and nonalcoholics.

In summary, many people who work extensively treating alcoholics are drawn to the conclusion that some "X" factor in their biology must be present which makes it impossible for them to be social drinkers, but this factor has as yet not been discovered.

2. Psychologic Theories

Other researchers in alcoholism feel that since no biologic peculiarities of alcoholics have been proven in spite of prolonged attempts to do so, the most likely cause of alcoholism lies in the psychologic area. This area can be divided into two parts—(A) studies of the familial background of alcoholics, and (B) studies of the alcoholic's own personality characteristics.

A. Familial Background of Alcoholics. The family backgrounds of 77 alcoholics were studied by Howard Clinebell[6] who carefully interviewed the alcoholics themselves regarding their home lives as children. He found that 57 percent of the alcoholics came from a home which could be regarded as severely inadequate. The four major parental characteristics in these homes were authoritarianism, success worship, moralism, and overt rejection. The first three of these characteristics are, in part, also subtle forms of rejection.

Robins, Bates, and O'Neal[7] did a 30-year follow-up study on 502 children who had been seen in a child guidance clinic and compared this group to matched controls who had never been treated in a clinic. They found that a significantly larger percentage of the ex-child guidance clinic patients developed alcoholism as compared to the matched controls. Antecedent factors evident in the childhood histories of the clinic patients found to be significantly related to alcoholism in later life were: very low family social status, parental inadequacy (particularly antisocial behavior on the part of fathers) and serious antisocial behavior of the patients themselves.

Amark[8] found a high rate of criminal behavior and alcoholism in the brothers of alcoholics and some evidence that the fathers also had a high rate of criminal activities. This would lend support to the theory that the antisocial family gives rise to alcoholism in the children.

Manfred Bleuler's study reported by Diethelm[5] was concerned with the family backgrounds of 50 well-to-do American alcoholics who were hospitalized at the Payne Whitney Clinic. He found that, even in this upper class group, 38 percent had "grossly unfavorable home environments" as children and 58 percent had long-standing contact with alcoholics before the age of 20.

The theme that runs through all of these studies is the strong tendency toward an unusual amount of psychopathology in the families of alcoholics. One would seem rather safe in saying that the alcoholics' family backgrounds provided at least part of the seed bed in which alcoholism grew.

B. Personality Characteristics of Alcoholics. Many studies have been completed on the psychologic characteristics of alcoholics themselves. Since most of these researches have been done after the person has developed alcoholism, only inferences can be made as to his personality before he became an alcoholic. The psychiatrists, Karl Menninger and Robert Knight, have written about the "alcoholic personality" and have depicted it as a rather clear-cut entity. However, after many psychological studies of alcoholics there is no general agreement that there is an alcoholic personality upon which alcoholism is extremely likely to develop. There are, though, certain characteristics[6] that do appear quite common in a majority of alcoholics, and various combinations of these characteristics may well have formed the seed bed in which alcoholism grew. These characteristics are (1) high level of anxiety in interpersonal relations; (2) emotional immaturity; (3) ambivalence toward authority; (4) low frustration tolerance; (5) grandiosity; (6) low self-esteem; (7) feeling of isolation; (8) perfectionism; (9) guilt; (10) compulsiveness; (11) angry over-dependency; (12) sex role confusion; (13) inability to express angry feelings adequately.

Alcohol's ability to reduce a *high level of anxiety in interpersonal relations* has caused Dr. Jellinek to dub alcohol "a social lubricant." Many alcoholics early in their disease use alcohol as a drug for calming anxious and insecure feelings which arise at a social gathering. As their disease progresses, they seem to become even less able to relate to people and therefore become even more dependent on alcohol to "get in the mood to relax and have fun." As will be further explained later, the alcoholic often feels he is not worthy of being loved or cared about; therefore, in a social gathering he feels insecure and out of place. Thus, as their inability to deal with people effectively becomes more pronounced, they need increasing amounts of alcohol to blot out this increasingly unpleasant reality. It has been my personal experience in a follow-up study of alcoholics treated in a military hospital[9] that the ones who have attained the longest period of sobriety are usually the ones who have noted the most improvement in ability to get along with their friends. Conversely, the ones who have been able to maintain little sobriety also note little improvement in ability to get along with their friends.

Emotional immaturity includes being excessively moody, demanding that one's desires be met promptly, having a violent temper, expressing one's emotions through acts rather than words, and being self-centered. Certainly some alcoholics can be described thusly. It is not certain, though, whether these alcoholics had always been this way or became this way only after their disease of alcoholism had become established.

Ambivalence toward authority as emphasized by Giorgio Lolli is an extremely prevalent symptom of alcoholics. A constant struggle goes on in many alcoholics between the need to be dependent and subservient and the need to be dominant and mighty. The common example is the alcoholic who married a domineering wife because of his need to be dependent on someone, and upon getting drunk beats her to prove he is really the dominant one.

Low frustration tolerance is part of emotional immaturity and is a common attribute of children, as well as alcoholics. It is this limited ability to stand frustration that often causes the alcoholic to resume drinking.

Grandiosity is present in the alcoholic when he is sober as well as drinking. Everyone knows of the alcoholic sitting in a bar who boasts to his drinking chums of the fantastic business deal he is about to close tomorrow. And when the alcoholic sobers up the next morning, he manifests the opposite side of the same coin. He states to his wife: "I'm the worst person in the world, I've failed in everything I've ever done." To be all that bad is no small accomplishment either. Grandiosity is a defense against feelings of guilt which obsess the alcoholic.

Low self-esteem is one of the important traits that helps alcoholics continue to drink. "When I drink I feel like a champ, a king, and the next morning I realize what a crumb I am," is how one alcoholic expressed it to me. This being the case, what a great temptation it is to have "just one more drink" to feel good again. Feelings of low self-esteem often stem from being emotionally neglected as a child. The alcoholic often feels he has never really been loved as he should have been, and probably is not really worth loving.

Feelings of isolation are the natural outgrowth of his inability to get along with people. As the alcoholic continues drinking, his behavior and conversation become less accept-

able to those about him and consequently his family and
friends begin isolating him from their social circle.

Perfectionism and *compulsiveness* are components of grandiosity. All three of these symptoms are largely an outgrowth
of intense feelings of *guilt*, feelings of being unloved and
unlovable. The alcoholic must prove that he is better than
his fellow man so that he will not have to feel so guilty about
his failures whenever he is sober. Therefore, he must do
things better than most people and consequently becomes
compulsive and perfectionistic.

Angry Over-Dependency. This characteristic of the alcoholic is actually one of the commonest and most basic. In
simple terms, many alcoholics do not grow up emotionally
but remain overly-dependent on one or the other parent such
as is normal for a youngster until the age of 13 or 14. This
failure to mature emotionally is due to rejection by one or
both parents. This rejection can take the form of either overt
neglect or over-protection and over-domination by the parents. These parental attitudes cause a literal arresting of
emotional growth at the early adolescent age level. The adult
alcoholic remains overly-dependent. He is painfully aware
of his excessive needs for attention, affection, praise, and his
being pampered and "babied." As a result, he is chronically
angry that these excessive demands are never fully met because his spouse or any other adult is unable to satisfy such
excessive dependency needs. Thus many alcoholics can accurately be described as angry over-dependent people.

Sex-role Confusion. One of the biggest conflicts present in
many alcoholics revolve around their manliness, womanliness,
or lack thereof. Over and over again in therapy, alcoholics
expand on the theme that alcohol makes them feel like the
real he-man or she-woman they always wanted to be. Along
with this he-manliness for example, goes sexual promiscuity
(Don Juan Syndrome), fighting, boasting, etc.

Inability to Express Angry Feelings Adequately. Alcoholics
are in general very sensitive people. Consequently they tend
to build up feelings of anger at even minor rejections or frustrations. In addition, they find it very hard to deal adequately
with this great wealth of angry feelings. They often find it
very difficult to "talk out" their feelings and therefore either

hold them inside or explosively let them out in an argument or fight. This particular characteristic is one of the biggest stumbling blocks to permanent recovery from their illness.

3. Socio-Cultural Theories

Understanding of the socio-cultural aspects of alcoholism is of great aid in placing the psychological and biochemical aspects of alcoholism in proper perspective, but as these factors are discussed in Chapter 1 they need not be reviewed here.

It is a fairly sound truism to assume that human beings in general try to successfully adjust to their environment. People who ultimately become alcoholics discovered at some point in their life what an aid alcohol appeared to be in helping them adjust successfully to their life. Alcohol is a drug with many appealing properties. It relieves anxiety and tension. It is an anesthetic which can relieve physical and emotional pain. It helps release inhibitions. It can be made into a tasty and readily available beverage.

It is no wonder then that people who find themselves in a chronically stressful situation which can be "temporarily relieved" by drinking alcohol gradually begin depending on alcohol as a source of relief. Whether the chronically uncomfortable situation stems from the individual's own psychological problems, whether it comes from chronic environmental stresses such as an unhappy marriage or extremely frustrating job, or whether it comes from chronic physical pain or poor health, alcohol offers temporary relief for all these conditions. Unfortunately though, alcohol is an addicting drug and as its use is repeated over the months and years, the drinker gradually develops alcoholism.

NATURAL HISTORY OF THE DISEASE ALCOHOLISM

Therefore the final approach to clarifying the psychiatric facets of alcoholism is to understand the natural history of the development of this disease. The four phases of progression of alcoholism as originally described by E. M. Jellinek[10] are these:

Phase I: The Pre-alcoholic Phase has two main features.

A. A person begins *meeting* everyday *tensions by drinking* but does not lose control and does not get drunk and is not regarded as a problem by anyone. He thus begins *using alcohol as a drug to treat* his "nerves" rather than a beverage consumed at a social occasion.

B. He begins drinking *larger* amounts of alcohol more often to gain the same effect he used to get from drinking less alcohol less often. This phase lasts from a few months to five or even ten years or more.

Phase II: The Early Alcoholic Phase (nonaddictive alcoholism) is characterized by the following.

A. *Blackouts* begin occurring. These are brief periods of amnesia which occur during or immediately following a drinking episode. Although the drinker may appear to be behaving normally, the next morning he will not remember what he did the previous evening. He begins worrying that he may have done something foolish during that period of time and therefore tries to avoid talking about that drinking episode. These blackouts become more and more frequent.

B. He begins *sneaking drinks*. This takes several forms. He may start having a few extra drinks at a party, gulping the first few drinks, drinking it "on the rocks," having a few drinks before the party begins and a "nightcap" afterward, etc.

C. He develops a *preoccupation* with alcohol. He becomes worried he won't get enough at a party, so he will bring his own bottle. He may start hiding the bottle to protect his supply.

D. He becomes plagued by *feelings of guilt* about his drinking behavior. He realizes his drinking has become abnormal and as a defense he becomes very angry and guilty when approached on the subject.

E. He consequently *avoids reference to alcohol* in conversation, particularly when sober. He tries desperately to deny that he has any problem with alcohol.

The person at this phase is called by many of his friends a "Heavy Drinker," but is not yet considered an alcoholic by them. But *the person himself and his immediate family* will realize things are getting out of control. He experiences fleeting insight into the fact that he is becoming sick and needs help. But he tends to rationalize this away. This phase lasts from six months to five years.

In order to continue drinking the alcoholic develops a characteristic set of alibis, or in psychiatric jargon, "mechanisms of defense." Three main defense mechanisms are used most commonly.

1. *Denial:* This is the most basic of the alcoholic's defense mechanisms. It is precisely his inability to face unpleasant reality which in the beginning leads him to use alcohol to blot out this unpleasant reality. And as his illness becomes progressively more severe, so must his denial become progressively stronger. An example of the alcoholic's denial is evident in the oft-quoted phrase "I can take it or leave it alone." It is painfully apparent to everyone else but the alcoholic that this statement is nothing more than an attempt at blanket denial of his great drinking problem.

2. *Rationalization:* When faced with reality, simple denial of the existence of a drinking problem is difficult to maintain. Therefore the process of rationalization, i.e., twisting the illogical around until it looks logical, is a handy device. An example is "It was a sunny hot day and when I finished mowing the yard I went to the icebox for a drink. When I saw that ice-cold beer there I knew that was the best thing I could take to quench my thirst." The obvious question one must ask is, "Wasn't there any icewater or soda-pop or milk or something else that would quench your thirst?"

3. *Projection:* Another overworked mechanism of defense when frank denial tends to break down is to project the guilt for drinking from the alcoholic to another person, usually a family member or employer. "If my wife would just quit nagging me about drinking too much I wouldn't do it anymore." Question: "Is there some unpleasant change that takes place in your personality when you drink that causes your wife to complain?"

Phase II can also be called the nonaddictive phase, as the alcoholic has become psychologically dependent on alcohol but has not become physically dependent. He can still control his drinking on any given occasion with great effort if he sets out to do this. But his drinking pattern is one of drinking too much, too often, resulting in all the previously mentioned symptoms of this phase, i.e., he begins developing new problems associated with drinking in the areas of his family, job, friends and health.

Phase III: The Crucial Phase—Addictive Alcoholism. It is during this period that the alcoholic either stops drinking or loses most everything that is near and dear to him. The most outstanding characteristic of this phase is *loss of control* over the use of alcohol. Any drinking of alcohol starts a type of short-circuit in which the person can't stop drinking. The urge for the second drink may be as short as a few minutes after the first drink or as long as a few weeks, but it eventually comes; and when it does, the person will continue drinking to the point of drunkenness. After the first drink he isn't thinking logically; "instead of thinking, he's drinking." Thus, if the person refrains from *taking that first drink*, which is within his voluntary control, he can break the self-perpetuating short-circuit.

The alcoholic's key to connecting this short-circuit is his frank denial that the first drink will harm him in any way. This denial is aided by the fact that in past years he could drink just one and stop, and he tenaciously tries to imagine that this is still the case.

It should be obvious that with all the pathologic mechanisms of defense and personality characteristics which have become apparent, the alcoholic's ability to adjust to life becomes extremely impaired. His family, employer, and friends chide him and quite probably will break relations with him. His great dependence on alcohol and his unwillingness to admit he has lost control over its use result in his trying many ways to get his drinking and his life under control. He will change his job, change his spouse, change his friends, change his drinking habits, change his place of living, change his doctor or minister, and so forth. But as long as he continues drinking, he *cannot change his ultimate down-hill course*.

Phase IV: The Final Phase. By this time, the alcoholic

has lost all that he formerly held near and dear to him. Characterstics of the end stage are:

1. *Benders:* He stays intoxicated for days at a time. These are unplanned drinking sprees whereas the drinking binges he has previously had he would plan for a weekend or some other convenient time.

2. His associations are now primarily with people far below his previous social level, often with skid-row derelicts.

3. He begins drinking any type of alcohol he can obtain, such as bay rum, shaving lotion, rubbing alcohol, etc.

4. He develops delirium tremens (D.T.'s), hallucinations, paranoid delusions, etc.

5. He develops severe medical complications such as cirrhosis of the liver, brain damage, and so forth.

In summary, it should be re-emphasized that alcoholism is an extremely complex illness. Although much is known about the psychiatric aspects of this illness, they can only be seen in their proper perspective when viewed in relation to the physical, social, and cultural aspects of the illness.

4

What Does It Cost To Be an Alcoholic?

E. HOLT BABBITT

THE DOLLARS ADD UP RAPIDLY WHEN JOE'S ON A BENDER

Dr. H. Mac Vandiviere writing in the March–April, 1961 issue of *Inventory* said ". . . It is, therefore, apparent that

REPRINTED with permission of *Inventory*, Vol. 11, No. 2, July–August, 1961.

alcoholism is not a simple disease. It is multiphasic in etiology (or cause); it is developmental, mental, physiologic and bio-chemical; and it is multiphasic in its signs, symptoms, and impact on the family and society . . ."

One multiphasic impact receiving little emphasis in dis-cussions of alcoholism is the financial involvement of the individual alcoholic. Most references to economic factors concerned with alcoholism mention the direct cost to industry, the amount spent for education of the public, treatment and research by the various governmental agencies and voluntary programs, and the overall estimated cost to society. Few words have been written concerning what it costs an *in-dividual* to drink excessively. This particular aspect has been neglected or de-emphasized in assessing economic, emotional, and physiological damage to the alcoholic. When an alcoholic takes that first drink, how much does it really cost him?

A study was recently conducted in two groups of patients at a treatment center for alcoholics in the Midwest which indicates that there may be a correlation between the severity of the alcoholic's drinking problem and how free spending he is when drinking.

Nine major categories of spending in which the alcoholic would be involved during the course of his progressive illness were set up and defined by the same counselor who inter-preted the findings. The indices for measuring the financial involvement of the individual alcoholic were applied in the regular schedule of group sessions at the treatment center. The counselor interpreted the indices to the patients and then asked the two groups to provide information relative to the nine categories for a twelve-month period prior to their admission. In some cases the previous calendar year was used.

The indices of measurement have not been put to a real test since they have only been used with two groups of patients in one treatment center and should, therefore, merely be regarded as a guide for determining the seriousness of financial involvement. Psychiatric evaluation, if necessary, psy-chological testing, physical examination, counseling and other criteria should be utilized in total evaluation of the drinking problem.

The nine categories of spending used in the study as indices of financial involvement follow:

1. *Direct Cost of Alcoholic Beverages.* This category includes beer, wine, whiskey and non-beverage products, too, if applicable. The cost of chasers or mixes, provided these were used, and money spent by others on drinks for the alcoholic individual are also included. (Although the categories are not listed in any particular rank order, this one unquestionably deserves billing as the top ranking expenditure for an alcoholic.)

2. *Loss of Wages.* This category includes days and hours off from work which directly or indirectly resulted from drinking. Unseen here by the casual observer and perhaps the alcoholic, too, is the loss of income from being out of work and the time between jobs. Sometimes a problem drinker may also take a pay cut when going back to work.

3. *Court Fines and Costs.* Bail and bond fees, attorney fees for court appearances, non-support costs, and fines for driving when intoxicated, public drunkenness, and assault and battery fall under this category which can also be broken down into a sub-category of factors associated with a broken marriage. The latter includes attorney fees for one or both parties for court costs, the expense of filing for divorce or separation, and the eventual payment of alimony or support money. Following the final action, if it does occur, a property settlement may be involved, along with previous bills, plus the ensuing expense of separate living quarters.

4. *Medical Care Costs.* Hospitalization following a bender, medications, the physician's visit to the home to treat the alcoholic in the withdrawal period, visits to the doctor's office, and emergency and long-term treatment for accidents and illnesses incurred while drinking are the cost factors of this category.

5. *Loss of Home and Furnishings or Place of Business.* This category, if the losses do occur during the progression of alcoholism, is very costly and can hike the alcoholic's expenditures way out of proportion. One alcoholic, in his prime working days, lost the management of an exclusive men's shop because of his drinking. As his illness worsened over the years, he went from job to job, city to city, finally ending

up clerking in another men's store. When last heard from, he had lost that job, too and had settled for spot jobs. True he didn't own the first haberdashery, but he had an excellent earning potential before drinking took precedence over his job.

6. *Accident Expenses.* Under this category come insurance costs (including financial liability), car repairs, medical expenses for injuries to oneself and others, and destruction of personal and public property. A lawsuit could rapidly increase the total of related expenses.

7. *Miscellaneous Expenses.* Some odd and assorted expenses are included in this category. To name a few—taxi fares, long distance telephone calls, extravagant buying, lavish dining and buying drinks "for the house." Many other sundry expenses could be included.

8. *Loss or Sale of Personal Belongings.* This category includes clothing, watches, wallets, pen and pencil sets, cigarette lighters, cameras, and radio or television sets. These items may have been lost through negligence and carelessness while drinking or they may have been sold outright for further purchase of liquor.

9. *Sale of Other Items.* Included in this category are automobiles, work tools, appliances and visits to pawn shops. Overlapping with category 8 could occur here, but nevertheless, the categories are listed separately.

10. *Other.* This category was set up as a catchall for expenditures not explained elsewhere.

ALLOWANCE FOR ALIBIS

Allowance has been made for the complex system of alibis an alcoholic uses and believes in. Open-ended questionnaires sometimes leave a few lines at the conclusion for items not listed specifically in structured questions. Category ten was provided just in case the alibiing permitted omission of certain expenditures.

It's reasonable to assume an alcoholic would try to rationalize his way out of some expenses incurred. For instance, he could claim no loss of wages from drinking because he was unemployed during the period involved. But why was he unemployed? He might claim that he spent no money for whiskey because he was in prison. But what led to his imprisonment?

Correlating the total expenditures compiled by any number of alcoholics with nonalcoholics would be of little value. Many nonalcoholics have a high liquor bill but, in general, it could be said that the expenditures of alcoholics would exceed those of non-alcoholics in most of the categories used due to the frequency and intensity of their drinking bouts and deeper financial involvements.

Now come the appalling figures. The collective estimate, even though representing only a portion of alcoholics seen in one treatment center for one year, is staggering and serves as a true "eye opener" of the enormity of the problem. Based on the nine major categories of spending, one group of males averaged $1,000 per man for the twelve months preceding admission. Another group totalled $32,000 for a two year period. If the pattern prevailed for the former group, a total of $50,000 would have accumulated over a five year period. By the time many chronic alcoholics are seen in a clinic or affiliate with Alcoholics Anonymous, it is apparent that alcoholism and economic deterioration have progressed hand in hand over the years.

The expenses of a person in the advanced stages of alcoholism will be most dramatic when, after a period of sobriety, he suffers a relapse and goes on a bender. Expenses in some categories are automatic and many alcoholics stand a good chance of rating in the minus column under all nine major categories.

The plateau or daily drinker deserves mention although his drinking pattern is less explosive than that of the chronic and periodic drinker. An alcoholic drinking a pint or more a day, day after day, will rapidly accumulate a bar bill approaching an awesome total.

Variations of individual totals, however, are innumerable. To illustrate this point and some of the expenses that could be incurred on a drinking spree, let's take a look at a hypothetical alcoholic's expense account while he is on a bender.

Joe is an average guy in his late forties. After fourteen months of sobriety, he goes on a bender that lasts over a week. He starts drinking after work on a Friday night and reaches his saturation point eight tortuous days and nights later. Let's take a look at Joe's expense account for this period:

The direct cost of alcoholic beverages which Joe consumed was $75.

As a good shoe salesman, Joe usually brought home $90 per week. He missed one week of work while on the bender and another recuperating from his drinking spree. Hence, Joe's loss of wages for the two weeks was $180.

So far, Joe's bender has cost him $255.

Fortunately, Joe's court fines and costs were not too expensive although he was in no shape to pay them. He received the minimum fine of $12 for two overtime parking tickets.

Joe has now spent $267.

At the end of the spree, Joe went to a hospital where he remained four days at a rate of $18 per day for a total cost of $72. Even though his insurance paid the bill, it's still accountable.

Joe's bender has now amounted to $339.

Joe incurred no losses pertaining to home and furnishings or place of business and had no accident expenses, but his miscellaneous expenses amounted to $60.

Joe's expense account has jumped to $399.

Joe's wife gave him an $80 watch when he celebrated one year of continuous sobriety. He pawned the watch during the bender and lost the pawn ticket. He also lost his wallet with $25 in it, bringing the cost of loss of personal belongings to $105.

Joe's accumulative expenses have now amounted to $504.

Shortly before his spree ended, the finance company repossessed the television set on which Joe had already paid $125.

Joe is now $629 in the red.

Any item which was lost, broken, or destroyed will probably be replaced eventually. And this will, of course, involve additional expense. Sooner or later Joe will probably buy a new watch, but this one won't be nearly as nice as the one he pawned—he'll pay about $19.98 for it, maybe. He is an avid baseball fan and loves to watch his favorite team in action on television. So, of course, there's the matter of a new television set, but this time Joe will probably settle for a $40 used model. Including $6 for cleaning the clothes he soiled, another $65.98 must be added to the $629 he has already spent.

The grand total for Joe's bender is $694.98—but we'll round it off at $695.

Figuring fifteen days of being out of commission and non-productive (eight days for drinking and seven for recuperation), this bender cost Joe $46.33 per day. He spent just over half of one week's pay during each day of his spree. Sure, he got his job back this time, but in the course of breaking his stretch of sobriety, Joe touched on seven of the nine major categories of spending.

Joe could rationalize his costly bender by saying that even though he had slipped he had remained sober for fourteen months. However, the slip was a monetary undoing. The progress he had made on his family budget and monthly payments was wiped out in two weeks. When averaged for fourteen months, Joe's bender amounted to $49.64 per month. If, in his quest for sobriety, Joe just couldn't remain sober and went on a drinking spree every fourteen months for 5.8 years (allowing for five sprees spaced fourteen months apart), he would spend a total of $3,475.

The financial involvement and economic chaos an alcoholic experiences is very difficult to measure and is, of course, relative and varies with each individual alcoholic. It can be said, however, that it costs money to drink whether the individual's drinking pattern is daily, weekend, or periodic. Dollars and cents add up rapidly for the alcoholic who has not taken a few moments to figure out how much one drink may cost him. Finance companies, loan sharks, pawn shops, banks and credit unions in addition to increasing dependence on relatives, friends, churches, and agencies are some of the sources that will inevitably be relied upon for assistance in the financial crises of alcoholics.

As alcoholism can be prevented, so can preventive steps be taken to avoid what Joe went through. If individuals who suspect that they are on the road to alcoholism would seek help early, their ultimate cash outlay for treatment would be far less than what a bender cost our hypothetical Joe or thousands like him. And, in all probability, they could avoid costly $695 slips.

PART III

Some Socio-Cultural

Aspects

of Alcoholism

5

Teen-Agers, Drinking, and the Law:
A Study of Arrest Trends for
Alcohol-Related Offenses

MURIEL W. STERNE, DAVID J. PITTMAN,
THOMAS COE

Not all alcohol-related offenses committed by youth are equally serious. Liquor law violations are largely an artifact of state laws prohibiting the sale of intoxicating beverages to persons under twenty-one. Studies of teen-age drinking behavior indicate that these laws fail to deter early experimentation with alcohol and often lack either parental or peer-group support. Lowering the age for legal purchase and consumption to eighteen would simplify liquor law enforcement, thereby releasing scarce police resources for the detection of serious crime. Juvenile arrests for other alcohol-related offenses rose 28 percent in St. Louis in 1950–1960, the increase suggesting the need for effective and intensive alcohol education in the secondary schools and cooperation between police and social work authorities for selective referral for treatment and re-education of those whose offenses warn of later serious behavior disorders and criminality. The nation's perennial concern for the welfare of its youth is manifested in a variety of well-intentioned, if not always well-conceived, ways. In examining alcohol-related offenses committed by persons under twenty-one, we find a convergence of two sources of concern related to youth: a

REPRINTED with permission of *Crime and Delinquency,* National Council on Crime and Delinquency, New York, January, 1965.

distrust of the effects of alcohol—especially, though not
exclusively, on the immature—and a concern for their law-
abidingness. Focusing on alcohol-related offenses committed
by juveniles and minors, this paper will present arrest statistics
from the 1950s and 1960s for the city of St. Louis to assess
whether all such offenses can be considered equally serious
and whether the laws relative to teen-age drinking succeed
in their intent.

By "alcohol-related offenses" we mean those offenses which
are committed frequently by persons under the influence of
alcohol[1] or which by their very nature are associated with
beverage alcohol. Examples of the first type are common
assault, disorderly conduct, and vagrancy; of the second type,
driving while intoxicated, public drunkenness, and liquor law
violations.[2] As a group, these offenses provide an estimate of
the extent to which law enforcement agencies are involved
with violations associated with the use of alcohol.

In judging the significance of alcohol-related offenses by
youth, it is useful to distinguish between those offenses which,
as an artifact of state liquor laws regarding access to alcoholic beverages, differentiate between adults and minors, and
those offenses for which both age groups are equally liable
to legal intervention. There is little argument about the
socially undesirable aspects of the latter category of alcohol-
related crimes, since offenses such as common assault, drunken
driving, and vagrancy are obviously hazardous to the well-
being of both the individual and the community. Since the
ingestion of alcoholic beverages by youth does not invariably
or even frequently have deleterious effects,[3-7] why do most
states forbid the sale of intoxicating beverages to anyone
under twenty-one? Behind these liquor laws lie the assumptions of American prohibitionism: that the use of alcohol
is sinful and dangerous, resulting in problem behavior, and
that drinking in any degree is equally undesirable, since
moderate social drinking is the forerunner of chronic inebriation. Therefore, legally blocking the young person's access
to alcoholic beverages guards him from the damaging consequences of drinking before he reaches maturity, at which
time he is expected to be fully responsible for his behavior.

FALLACIES IN LAWS ON ALCOHOL

There are several fallacies in this approach. The first is the belief that maturity (in reference to these laws) occurs at age twenty-one. Confusion as to when maturity begins is exemplified by the discrepancies in age at which different types of adult behavior are legally permissible. In Missouri, for example, a car may be driven by a person of sixteen; cigarettes may be smoked in public at eighteen; marriage without parental consent is legal for females at eighteen and for males at twenty-one; juvenile status ends at sixteen, and at seventeen the minor is tried as an adult for any offense he has committed. In Georgia and Kentucky the eighteen-year-old is allowed to vote but is barred from the purchase of spirits. Even more confusing to the young person is the fact that he may have to perform many of the duties of an adult before reaching ᵗhe age of twenty-one. With parental consent a young man becomes eligible for military service at seventeen. While still in his teens he may have a full-time job and be the head of a household, indicating that he has shouldered the main responsibilities of adulthood. Under these circumstances, how incongruous to prohibit his purchase of alcoholic beverages until he is twenty-one!

The second fallacy is the belief that the law is an effective deterrent to early experimentation with alcohol. Teen-agers perceive alcohol predominantly as a beverage for use in social situations rather than as a drug; they associate drinking with "coming of age" or assuming adult roles. Drinking is viewed as typically adult behavior; adulthood, in turn, is associated with the assumption of "adultlike roles rather than the achievement of a particular age (Notes 8, 5, pp. 236–237). Teen-agers' conceptions of "coming of age" are illustrated by high-school graduation, full time employment, marriage, or service in the armed forces. It should come as no surprise, therefore, that studies of high-school students have found that anywhere from one-third to four-fifths have had some experience with the use of alcoholic beverages, with the average age of first exposure probably being fourteen or fifteen. Furthermore, between one-third and two-thirds of these teen-age users had their first drinking experience at home with relatives present, suggesting that for many parents the question of teen-age drinking is one of timing and control rather than of abstinence. Finally, it has been found that drinking increases with age, with the peak for the teen-ager in both intensiveness and extensiveness of drinking coming at the age of eighteen, which normally coincides with graduation from high school. Teen-age claims to parental permission to drink in and away from home also tend to increase with age. Apparently, laws aimed at discouraging teen-age drinking often lack either parental or peer-group support and are widely violated.

Of course, the failure of legislative regulation of drinking behavior is not confined to the teen-ager but is a more general problem in our society. In a recent examination of the New York State Alcoholic Beverage Control Law, the Moreland Commission points out that the assumptions behind liquor laws—that they promote temperance and reduce excessive drinking—are unsubstantiated. "On the contrary, industry records of per capita consumption show that from 1934–1962 it has approximately trebled although virtually all states have some form of control . . ." (Note 9, p. 3). Furthermore, regulation of alcoholic beverage distribution does not adequately cope with the gamut of serious social problems associated with alcohol use and "creates a false sense of controlling much that is beyond the control of a liquor outlet licensing system" (Note 6, p. 3).

Similarly, liquor laws aimed at teen-agers not only fail in their intent; they also produce questionable consequences:

1. The consumption of alcohol in automobiles is clearly undesirable, yet in denying the right of the older teen-ager to its public purchase and consumption, we unwittingly suggest this combination.

2. The practice of patterned evasion of stringent liquor laws is a poor introduction of youth to adult civic responsibility, suggesting adult roles which incorporate neither respect for nor conformity to the law.

3. As Prohibition amply demonstrated, liquor laws which do not meet with public acceptance provide illicit business opportunities. While taverns have not been found to be an important factor producing delinquency, a small minority of them capitalize on this opportunity for illicit business, catering to the teen-age trade, seldom checking ages, and sometimes providing questionable entertainment and an outlet for drugs.[10] Attracted, perhaps, by the prestige gained through illegal drinking, delinquents are more likely than non-delinquents to frequent these taverns, where they come in contact with further unwholesome influences.

Teen-age violations of liquor laws are a consequence of the rigid definition of maturity. The enforcement of a law that lowered the legal age for the purchase and possession of alcoholic beverages to eighteen would be simpler and would contribute to a more effective allocation of scarce police resources for the prevention and detection of socially serious crime.

OFFENSES BY PERSONS UNDER TWENTY-ONE

Table 1 shows the relative contribution of persons twenty and under to the total number of alcohol-related offenses committed in St. Louis during a three-year period. In 1960, persons aged ten through twenty made up 15 per cent of the city's population.[11] Since on the average, 11 per cent of all alcohol-related offenses were committed by youth, it is clear that they do not contribute disproportionately to this type of offense. The picture is different for specific offense categories, however. Approximately 23 percent of liquor law violations and 19 per cent of arrests for common assault were attributable to juveniles and minors. They are not over-represented in any other offense category, however—accounting for about 12 per cent of disorderly conduct and vagrancy arrests, 3 per cent of drunken driving arrests, and 2 per cent of arrests for public intoxication. Of course, some offenses have been found to be age-graded in frequency of occurrence, such as public drunkenness, which is most regularly seen in persons

Table 1. Involvement of Persons Twenty and Under in Alcohol-Related Offenses, St. Louis, Mo., 1957–1959

| | Number of Arrests | | | | | | Per Cent Represented by Those Twenty and Under | | |
| | Twenty and Under | | | All Ages | | | | | |
Offense	Male	Female	Total	Male	Female	Total	Male	Female	Total
Liquor Laws									
1957	82	34	116	349	134	483	23.5	23.5	24.0
1958	103	39	142	529	203	732	19.5	19.2	19.4
1959	177	56	233	626	236	862	28.3	23.7	27.0
Common Assault									
1957	145	28	173	746	183	929	19.4	15.3	18.6
1958	226	31	257	1,144	239	1,383	19.8	13.0	18.6
1959	182	29	211	956	181	1,137	19.0	16.0	18.6
Disorderly Conduct									
1957	1,127	302	1,429	9,302	2,994	12,296	12.1	10.1	11.6
1958	1,579	393	1,972	12,164	3,660	15,824	13.0	10.7	12.5
1959	1,482	457	1,939	12,073	3,744	15,817	12.3	12.2	12.3
Vagrancy									
1957	226	28	254	1,907	90	1,997	11.9	31.1	12.7
1958	207	17	224	1,857	152	2,009	11.1	11.1	11.1
1959	127	4	131	1,175	36	1,211	10.8	11.1	10.8
Driving While Intoxicated									
1957	24	—	24	722	33	755	3.3	—	3.2
1958	22	—	22	869	35	904	2.5	—	2.4
1959	29	1	30	812	52	864	3.6	1.9	3.5

Drunkenness									
1957	71	18	89	2,723	347	3,070	2.6	5.2	2.9
1958	55	9	64	2,725	336	3,061	2.0	2.7	2.1
1959	60	6	66	2,849	284	3,133	2.1	2.1	2.1
All Alcohol-Related Offenses									
1957	1,675	410	2,085	15,749	3,781	19,530	10.6	10.8	10.7
1958	2,192	489	2,681	19,288	4,625	23,913	11.4	10.6	11.2
1959	2,057	553	2,610	18,491	4,533	23,024	11.1	12.2	11.3

SOURCE: St. Louis Metropolitan Police Department, *Annual Report*, 1957, 1958, and 1959.

thirty and over.[1] Driving while intoxicated is less apt to occur among younger persons and is apt to be under-reported for all age groups because of the difficulty of enforcing the Missouri ordinance without verification of intoxication through either a breath test or a blood test.[12]

Although the involvement of young persons in liquor law violations is an artifact of current legislation, their contribu-

TABLE 2.   Arrests of Juveniles and Minors for Alcohol-Related-Offenses, St. Louis, Mo. 1950–60

| | Number of Arrests | | |
Offense	1950	1960	Per Cent Change
Liquor Laws			
Juveniles	–	82	–
Minors	8	223	+2688
TOTAL	8	305	+3713
Common Assault			
Juveniles	41	136	+ 232
Minors	309	108	− 65
TOTAL	350	244	− 30
Disorderly Conduct			
Juveniles	116	688	+ 493
Minors	877	862	− 2
TOTAL	993	1,550	+ 56
Vagrancy			
Juveniles	1	72	+7100
Minors	10	97	+ 870
TOTAL	11	169	+1436
Driving While Intoxicated			
Juveniles	–	4	–
Minors	12	26	+ 117
TOTAL	12	30	+ 150
Drunkenness			
Juveniles	3	15	+ 400
Minors	40	42	+ 5
TOTAL	43	57	+ 33
All Alcohol-Related Offenses			
Juveniles	161	997	+ 519
Minors	1,256	1,358	+ 8
TOTAL	1,417	2,355	+ 66

SOURCE: St. Louis Metropolitan Police Department, *Annual Report*, 1949, 1950, 1951, 1959, 1960, 1961. Figures for 1950 and 1960 represent means for 1949–1951 and 1959–1961 respectively. A juvenile is legally defined in Missouri as being sixteen years of age or below; a minor, as being between the ages of seventeen and twenty.

tion to common assault, vagrancy, and disorderly conduct arrests merits close attention. From 1950 to 1960, the number of arrests of juveniles and minors rose for all alcohol-related offenses, except common assault (Table 2). Since the decline in this offense category may simply be a consequence of under-reporting or the use of other classifications, such as disorderly conduct or vagrancy, the number of offenses for all categories was totaled. Comparison of 1950 and 1960 shows an overall increase of 66 per cent in arrests, with a slight increase for minors and a sharp one for juveniles. The 66 per cent increase is very high, especially since the size of the population aged ten to twenty in St. Louis City did not change appreciably during the decade. Seen in the standardized form of rates (Table 3), juveniles again account for most of the sharp rate rise over the decade, although their arrest rate is less than half that of minors. Despite the fact that minors show a 9 per cent decline in the number of arrests and the smallest increase in arrest rate,[13] their rate of arrest for alcohol-related offenses outstrips even that of adults.

How can these trends be accounted for? First, the great increase in liquor law violations should be attributed not to a change in youthful behavior but to a change in definitions of illegal behavior. Periodic drifts in the attention of legislative and law enforcement officials, in which different areas of crime come under scrutiny and new measures are adopted to deal with these offenses, have their impact on arrest frequencies. A more stringent version of the liquor laws, adopted in 1959 in Missouri, made it a misdemeanor for anyone under the age of twenty-one to purchase, attempt to purchase, or *have in possession* intoxicating liquor, or to purchase or attempt to purchase nonintoxicating beer.[14] Undoubtedly this has had its impact on the rise in liquor law violations.

Secondly, the seemingly drastic shift in juvenile behavior over the decade is related to a change in the administrative procedure of the St. Louis City Police Department, which now emphasizes formal rather than informal means of social control over this population segment. By 1953 the Juvenile Division of the Police Department had switched its emphasis

TABLE 3. Number and Rate of Arrests for Alcohol-Related Offenses,
St. Louis, Mo., 1950–1960, by Age

Age Grouping	Number of Arrests		Per Cent Change	Arrest Rate*		Per Cent Change
	1950	1960		1950	1960	
10–16**	161	915	+468	240	1,240	+417
17–20	1,248	1,135	− 9	2,793	2,989	+ 7
21+	12,669	13,850	+ 9	2,071	2,826	+ 36

*Per 100,000 of age grouping specified. Based on mean number of arrests for alcohol-related offenses, 1949–1951 and 1959–1961,
exclusive of liquor law violations.
**The arrest rate for persons aged ten to sixteen is slightly inflated since it is based on alcohol-related offenses committed by persons
sixteen and under. The contribution of persons below age ten would be negligible, however.

from police athletic leagues to the careful recording of juvenile offenses, on the grounds that social work functions should be left to those professionally trained in this field and that the most effective police contribution would be the apprehension of offenders and accurate reporting of offenses. Taking this policy change into account, we reanalyzed 1953 and 1959 juvenile arrest statistics for alcohol-related offenses. This time the rise was only 28 per cent, in marked contrast to the 468 per cent rise previously reported (Table 3)! This discrepancy illustrates the impact of administrative changes in law enforcement procedures and serves as a caution in the interpretation of juvenile delinquency statistics. However, given the preciseness of reporting by the St. Louis Police Department, this increase of 28 per cent is significant.

RECOMMENDATIONS

The above considerations have led us to make the following recommendations concerning laws and interagency coordination pertaining to teen-age drinking:

1. States should revise their liquor laws to accord more realistically with the facts of teen-age drinking. Police time could be better focused on the drinking violations of persons under eighteen.

2. At the same time, statutes regarding alcohol education should be reappraised with a view toward vigorously encouraging its inclusion in the secondary school curriculum. Since the majority of teen-agers will not be abstainers upon reaching adulthood, exclusive concentration on the possible ill effects of alcohol consumption is not enough. Also needed is a positive form of education which will inform the teen-ager about the effects of increasing doses of alcohol on the human being and which will relate this information to the necessity of drinking in a responsible manner, if one does drink.

3. The 28 per cent rise in 1950–1960 in St. Louis juvenile arrests for alcohol-related offenses and the high arrest rate of minors for these offenses suggest that an intensive coopera-

tive effort between police and social work authorities is necessary. Police emphasis on accurate detection and reporting of
offenses by youth should be encouraged, and these reports
should be used as a basis for selective referrals for treatment
and re-education. Youth agencies should be aware that repeated drinking violations by those below eighteen, and
other types of alcohol-related offenses committed by youths
of any age which come to the attention of police authorities
are frequently early warning signs of later behavior disorders
and criminal offenses.

6

Drinking Patterns and Alcoholism
Among American Negroes

MURIEL W. STERNE

Despite the fact that Negroes are the largest ethnic minority
in the United States and have been known as the minority
group with the highest rate of social problems over the longest time period, there have been few attempts at systematic
study of behavior patterns and value orientations in the
Negro subculture conducive to social deviance or personal
pathology. Yet blanket assumptions that the effects of racial
discrimination and low socio-economic status account for the
observed deviations obscure the fact that social pathologies
appearing on a patterned, subcultural basis may contribute
to the perpetuation of that same depressed socio-economic

THIS article is based on research supported by a grant from the
National Institute of Mental Health, U.S. Public Health Service
(MH-09189), "Social and Community Problems in Public Housing
Areas."

position. As such, the forms these pathologies take, and the content of the system of beliefs, values, and behaviors from which they stem, are in themselves valid objects for study.

The drinking of alcoholic beverages is a culturally-patterned behavior which may or may not be associated with social deviance, as deviance is defined in white, middle-class America. Where drinking is accompanied by deviance, damage to the drinker, to those in his immediate surroundings or to the larger society may occur in the form of alcoholism, excessive or problem drinking, or alcohol-related offenses. Obviously damage is experienced more literally for some of these, such as drunken driving, than for others where it may take the more attenuated form of violating the legal norms, as in purchases of alcoholic beverages by persons under age 21. Alcoholism takes various forms cross-culturally,[1, 2] but its most typical and troublesome form in the United States presumably involves addictive drinking with complex personality changes and serious organic pathology. Ideally, criteria assessing Negro drinking pathologies would be based upon this standard; in fact, a range of definitions of alcoholism is evident in the studies reviewed here. Excessive or problem drinking are impressionistic terms usually connoting the use of alcohol in amounts or in ways that produce impaired role performance. For our purposes, problem drinking involving the commission of arrestable offenses has been maintained as a separate conceptual entity. Alcohol-related offenses involve those which are by their very nature associated with beverage alcohol—public drunkenness, driving while intoxicated, liquor law violations—and offenses frequently committed by individuals under the influence of alcohol—disorderly conduct and vagrancy.[3] Studies of arrests or incarcerations for these charges, as well as inquiries into the association of drinking with other offense categories are also examined.

Alcoholism and other forms of problem drinking should not be studied out of the context of the drinking customs and larger culture and social structure from which they arise. The drinking custom is itself socially defined in terms of who drinks what (if anything), when and where, how much, with what effects, and for what reasons. Accordingly, studies of

American drinking behavior and attitudes[4-9] show variations in terms of social and demographic variables—age, sex, rural-urban residence, religious affiliation, ethnicity, and socio-economic status or its principal components (education, occupation, income). Furthermore, while the etiology of alcoholism is still an open question,[10] characteristics of the social structure and culture have been pointed out as influencing alcoholism rates and the extent of inebriety cross-culturally, both for industrialized and nonindustrialized societies and within American ethnic subcultures. Where the data permit, several of these dimensions are explored, specifically:

1. Normative orientations toward alcohol use: Bales[11] has delineated possible cultural attitudes. Alcohol can serve a *ritualistic* function, being used ceremonially as in *rites de passage* and religious observances. Snyder[12] has related the ritualistic definition of alcohol use among Orthodox Jews to this group's low alcoholism rate. Alcohol can also be used to promote *conviviality*, lowering restraints in social interaction. Bales[13] and Glad[14] have described this orientation as prevalent among Irish and Irish-American males. *Convivial* drinking incorporates both ritualistic and utilitarian elements, tending to symbolize solidarity and also to emphasize pleasurable feeling states. When convivial drinking occurs in highly developed form, there is some risk of its deterioration into purely utilitarian drinking, according to Bales.[13] In the *utilitarian* orientation toward alcohol use, drinking serves predominantly individual rather than social motives, as in the satisfaction or relief of self-contained needs or to gain some personal advantage over others. Bales[13] and Madsen[15] have linked the use of alcohol as the technique of choice for managing acute adjustment needs to high alcoholism rates. Finally, where the orientation toward alcohol use is one of *abstinence*, alcohol is not admitted to have positive functions; its use is considered extremely disruptive both socially and personally. Thorner[16] has discussed the relationship of religious asceticism to abstinence. Straus and Bacon[17] and Skolnick[18] have related membership in Protestant denominations endorsing abstinence to relatively high rates of complications with alcohol, for those who begin drinking.

2. Tolerance for intoxication and intoxication-related behaviors: Lemert[19] and Trice[20] have discussed how the American definition of the excessive drinker as an object of social rejection contributes to the development of alcoholism, with its progressive isolation, internalization of guilt and negative self-definitions by the drinker. From this standpoint, deviance may be viewed as an interactive process, resulting not only from the drinker's behavior, but also from social response to that behavior. Lemert[19] and Heath,[21] among others, have described situations in which drinking is widespread, the drunken person is not an object of censure or exclusion from the group, and alcoholic complications are rare or unknown.

3. Culturally consistent,[22] stable drinking customs for which there is consensus: Ullman[23] (Note 23, p. 50) has hypothesized that:

in any group or society in which the drinking customs, values and sanctions—together with the attitudes of all segments of the group or society—are well established, known to and agreed upon by all, and are consistent with the rest of the culture, the rate of alcoholism will be low.

Conversely, where:

the individual drinker does not know what is expected or when the expectation in one situation differs from that in another, it can be assumed that he will have ambivalent feelings about drinking. Thus, ambivalence is the psychological product of unintegrated drinking customs.

Myerson[24] and Bacon[25] have vividly described this ambivalence in the American culture. Ethnic subcultures and societies have been studied in which drinking customs were stable, well-agreed upon, and consistent with other cultural values, and where alcoholism was not a problem.[12, 26-29] However, Lemert[30] takes issue with Ullman's inference that alcoholic drinking develops in societies where the drinking practices are culturally inconsistent, and Simmons[31] while documenting an instance in which drinking is highly valued and pervasive in adult interpersonal relationships and brings with it few complications, nonetheless finds evidence of ambivalence about drinking and relates it to stresses in adult interpersonal relations and to the respect relations governing interaction between adults and youths. There is some question, therefore, as to whether the variables that Ullman links together operate independently of specific socio-cultural milieus or, indeed, are significant to the genesis of alcoholism.

A review of the literature regarding alcohol use among American Negroes suggests the preponderance of studies concerned with alcoholism, problem drinking, or alcohol-related offenses, and the dearth of systematic inquiries into what constitutes normal drinking behavior for this ethnic group. The American bias toward associating alcohol use with social problems is even stronger where Negroes are concerned, dating back to the early nineteenth century. At that time laws motivated in part by fears of slave uprisings were enacted in many states to prohibit Negroes, both slave and free, from purchasing or selling alcoholic beverages.[32-35] Today this bias manifests itself in different forms, but is no less apparent. For instance, the assertion we are about to document, that Negro drinking is generally associated with a higher rate of problems than is drinking by whites, is based on rates of alcoholism and other drinking problems calculated *as if* the proportion of drinkers to abstainers in the Negro and white populations were roughly equivalent, and *as if* the proportions of certain drinker types (such as heavy drinkers, who seem to run a higher-than-average risk of becoming alcoholic[36]) to all drinkers within the respective populations were about the same. Yet, in the absence of base rates for drinking among American Negroes, these assumptions are untested and may be erroneous. Should they underestimate the prevalence of Negro drinking and heavy drinking, and hence also the size of the risk group, the rate of problems associated with alcohol use would at the same time be exaggerated. In other words, these are not drinker-specific rates. Thus biases in what is or is not studied may beget biases in what is found.

Alcoholism and Problem Drinking

Evaluation of studies of alcoholism[37-64] and excessive or problem drinking[54, 65, 66] is complicated by the varied criteria for these phenomena, diverse sampling methods, intensive investigation of populations in several states to the complete neglect of others, and a concentration of studies around institutionalized populations. Therefore generalizations from these data must be tentative.

Despite some evidence to the contrary[41, 44, 45, 58, 61, 63, 65] most studies suggest that alcoholism rates, whether crude or age-standardized, are generally higher for Negroes than for whites, as are problem drinking rates. Since five of the disconfirming studies deal with data gathered from the 1920s through the 1940s, more recent studies[37, 38, 48–50, 55–57, 63, 65, 66] were singled out for scrutiny. In only two of these[63, 65] are Negro rates lower or the same as white rates; and one,[65] dealing with symptoms implicative of incipient alcoholism, is limited to a specialized age group, adolescents. For several of the more recent and carefully-controlled studies, Negro alcoholism rates are two to four times higher than white rates.[37, 48, 50, 55, 57] Focusing on nonhospitalized populations, similar rate discrepancies are also evident in alcoholism research at other kinds of institutional facilities such as outpatient psychiatric clinics,[37, 49] and in studies unaffected by who seeks or is accepted for treatment of alcoholism—alcoholism mortality rates for industrial policyholders of a major life insurance company,[56] alcoholism detected via a community health survey,[38] and rejection rates for military service in World War II in the Boston area.[43] Rowntree, McGill, and Hellman[61] also found Negro rejection rates for alcoholism greatly exceeded those of whites, but that the prevalence rate of alcoholism was lower among Negroes examined for military service, suggesting the possibility of greater deterioration among the Negro alcoholics. Furthermore when at least partial controls are instituted for socio-economic status,[38, 40, 46, 48, 50] migration status,[52] and for urbanization,[50, 53] Negro alcoholism rates are still in excess of those of whites.

Where studies touch on alcoholism in Negro females, the results are unequivocal. With the exception of Jellinek and Keller[44] who estimate the size of the alcoholic population on the basis of a formula whose validity has since been challenged,[68] rates of alcoholism for Negro females are uniformly higher than those of white females.[37, 38, 48, 50, 54-56, 64] Controlled for education, urban female rates are higher at each educational level for Negroes than for whites, ranging from three to six times higher.[48, 50] This discrepancy between Negro and white female rates rises with increasing educational attainment. Controlled for employment status, age-adjusted rates of employed Negro females are over three times higher than those of employed white females; for Negro females keeping house, the rate is 5.5 times higher than that of white females also keeping house.[50]

Although Negro and white females always reflect a lower alcoholism rate than the males of their respective races, the sex ratio of alcoholic males to females differs considerably by race. The ratio for Negroes is much lower than for whites,[37, 38, 48, 50, 51, 54-56, 64] so that Negro females run a much higher risk of incurring alcoholism, relative to Negro males, than do white females compared to white males. Part of this risk differential may be attributable to variation in hospitalization practice.[50, 55] White female alcoholics remain in the community longer than do their Negro counterparts. Studies taking careful account of both alcoholic in- and out-patients,[48, 49] and others not based on hospitalized populations[38, 56] suggest that the difference in risk is actual, however. Furthermore where rate changes in alcoholism among Negroes are explored,[55, 56] Negro females appear to be definitely disadvantaged relative to Negro males, with much slower declines in alcoholism or alcoholism mortality rates than males. Rates for white females do not show comparable tendencies.

What accounts for the comparatively vulnerable position of the Negro female? Possibly white and Negro females at the same socio-economic level experience different expectations with regard to their assumption of economic and familial roles, and also with respect to the use of alcohol. Bailey, Haberman, and Alksne (Note 38, p. 28) offer some support for this explanation, finding that Negro women were "more often heads of households and carried major responsibility as family breadwinners" than other women in their sample, and also noting from a participant observer's reports that Negro bars in a section of New York City resembled "neighborhood clubs with equal attendance by men and women and an atmosphere of camaraderie." Knupfer[7] makes a more explicit connection between social pressure against unrestrained drinking by women as a means of abetting their sexual restraint, and the ability of men to gain compliance with these behavioral standards by virtue of women's economic dependence. Therefore in groups where women are less often economically dependent on men, their behavior should more closely resemble that of men. For this reason the risk group for the development of alcoholism may be proportionately larger among Negro than white females.

Negroes also appear to experience institutional contact for or as a result of alcoholism earlier than do whites.[37, 47−51, 55, 62] To what extent does this reflect differentials in hospitalization practice, or differentials in the age of onset of alcoholism? Several studies of nonhospitalized populations[37, 49, 62] favor the latter conclusion. While Locke, Kramer, and Pasamanick[50] note hospitalization may be sought at an earlier age owing to the unavailability in the home of caretakers, they also suggest as alternatives that: 1. Diversion of what is at best a marginal income for purchasing alcoholic beverages involves curtailment elsewhere, perhaps in nutrition. Vitamin deficiencies may hasten the effects of alcohol and bring about earlier hospitalization; and that 2. Alcoholic release may be sought at a younger age. Earlier termination of schooling and entry into the job market have drinking correlates: "They become 'men' earlier and have to face men's problems earlier. At the same time, movement into the working world permits freer drinking" (Note 50, p. 464).

Migration of younger Negroes into areas where this age differential in alcoholism has been found is another possibility. Malzberg[52, 54] and Pittman and Gordon[3] have suggested that social and economic factors accompanying migration favor a higher incidence of alcoholism or excessive drinking. On the other hand, Landis and Page[46] observed an excess in rate of Negro to white admissions for alcoholic psychoses despite the indigenous character of the Negro population, and Locke and Duvall[48] found no significant difference in alcoholism hospitalization rates for nonwhites between native

Ohioans and those born elsewhere. However white native Ohioans had substantially lower rates than white in-migrants. The influence of migration in and of itself is therefore unclear.

In examining criminal statistics we are faced with additional pitfalls to valid inference. Wheeler[69] has suggested that criminal statistics reflect the commission of illegal acts by offenders only in part. Differentials in the definition of the act as grounds for complaint by victims or other interested citizens as well as differentials in police action also affect these statistics in unknown ways. Skolnick[70] suggests that there are regional differences in arresting practices of the police. Pittman and Gordon[3] describe Negroes as more vulnerable to arrest both as objects of racial discrimination and, since predominantly of lower class status, as members of the social class most subject to police action. This was supported in part for public intoxication arrests when controls for ecological social class area were instituted,[70] since this procedure narrowed the gap between Negro and white rates of arrest for public intoxication from 3.4 to 1.7 times higher for Negroes. Despite these limitations, studies of official arrest or incarceration records are of sociological value since the consequences of being defined as "criminal" are different from those experienced by persons not subjected to arrest for the very same behaviors.

Offenses Related to Drinking

Studies of alcohol-related offenses suggest much the same generalizations that are made in relation to alcoholism. Rates of arrest, conviction or incarceration for public intoxication tend to be higher for Negroes than for whites.[3, 70–75] In order to obtain more widespread coverage—since three of these studies center about the same locality[3, 72, 75]—crime reports for the United States as a whole were analyzed for the years 1958 through 1964.[76] During that time Negroes accounted for between 22 and 25 percent of the combined total of Negro and white public intoxication arrests; yet they represent 10.5 percent[77] of the American people (Note 77, Table 44). They were also disproportionately represented in other alcohol-related offense categories, accounting for approximately 15 percent of drunken driving arrests, one-fifth to one-third of liquor law violations, roughly 27 percent of vagrancy arrests, and one-third to two-fifths of disorderly conduct arrests.[76]

Public intoxication studies do not invariably report higher Negro rates, however.[78-80] Data relating to teen-agers is particularly contradictory. While two studies report substantially higher rates for Negro youth,[72, 75] another suggests that they are less likely to have been arrested for public intoxication.[80] In addition, two studies dealing with delinquent youth specifically[65, 81] indicate that Negro delinquents are less likely than white delinquents to manifest alcohol-related behaviors that are potentially arrestable offenses. National data on youthful offenses for 1964 offer contrasting evidence for different alcohol-related offense categories (Note 76, 1965, pp. 114–116): Negro youth accounted for approximately 13 percent of the public intoxication arrests of persons under age 18, which is proportional to their representation in this age grouping of the general population (Note 77, Table 46). However they accounted for proportionally fewer liquor law violations and drunken driving arrests (roughly 5 percent of each) and more disorderly conduct and vagrancy arrests (approximately one-fourth and one-third of each, respectively).

With the exception of Lightfoot[71] and Zax, Gardner and Hart,[75] the available studies either exclude females, or the incidence of female arrests and incarcerations on alcohol-related charges is so low as to make Negro-white comparisons in this area meaningless. For national statistics, cross-tabulations by race and sex are unavailable. For the two cited studies, Negro female rates again greatly exceeded those of white females, and the ratio of males to females was again much lower in the Negro group.

Where ages of Negro and white public intoxication offenders are compared, the Negro population is invariably significantly younger than the white.[3, 72, 74, 75, 82] In one of these,[72] almost all Negro intoxication offenders fell within the age range 20–59; two-thirds were between the ages of 30–49. For whites the range was 30–69, with two-thirds between the ages of 40–59. However the age profile for Negroes and whites incarcerated for nonalcohol-related offenses was almost identical, suggesting that public intoxication is in fact an earlier occurrence among the Negroes in the population studied. A corollary finding is that Negroes develop multiple arrest records for public intoxication at a younger age than whites.[75]

Alcohol use may of course be associated with the commission of offenses other than those discussed above. Its relationship to a more serious offense category, criminal homicide, has been investigated by Wolfgang and Strohm[83] who found for a sample of 588 cases that alcohol was present as a factor in the homicide situation significantly more often in cases involving Negroes than whites (70 percent vs. 49 percent), and that this relationship held whether analyzed from the standpoint of alcohol in the offender, the victim, or both, and for victims of either sex. The authors caution against drawing causal inferences about the relationship of drinking to criminal homicide, observing that most drinking does not result in the commission of serious crimes, and also point out that observed differences between races may reflect differences in base rates of drinking such that the higher incidence of alcohol-associated criminal homicide among Negroes may be a function of a higher incidence of drinking among this group in the general population.

Several studies have focused on selected characteristics of persons committing alcohol-related offenses.[74, 82, 84] Findings for male incarcerates of the District of Columbia Workhouse[74, 82] reflect greater social integration of the Negro than of the white public intoxication offender. Significantly higher proportions of Negroes were shown to be functioning members of their consanguine groups and participants in a broader interactional network not limited to a "skid-row" type subsociety. They were also more likely to perceive parents, siblings, and wives as either unopposed or less opposed to drinking, more likely to have used alcohol with relatives during the interval of their heaviest alcohol use, and less likely to have lost friends due to drinking. This suggests a greater acceptance of inebriation or the inebriate in the Negro subculture.

In a somewhat different vein, Negro offenders whose arrest history is characterized by a pattern of "drunk and assault" charges are compared with Negro offenders reflecting other arrest patterns.[84] "Drunk-and-assault" offenders were significantly more likely to have grown up in homes with a rigid, fundamentalistic background whose values were enforced by strict, dominating fathers, to have experienced and maintained close primary group ties, and to have come from less criminogenic environments. The "drunk and assault" pattern is interpreted in light of these findings as reflecting relative success of parental efforts at character development "so that this group could manifest hostility only after alcohol had weakened inhibitions, at which time a rather explosive outburst of violence generally occurred."

To summarize, the evaluation of data from studies of alcoholism, excessive or problem drinking, and offenses connected to alcohol use is hampered by their many methodological inadequacies. Nevertheless the weight of evidence points to a high prevalence among American Negroes of problems associated with drinking. Lacking systematic information regarding the prevalence of drinking in this group as a whole, no definitive statement can be made as to whether the problem rate is primarily a function of the size of the risk group or of other subcultural factors.

Drinking Patterns

Historical treatments of slavery in the United States contain the earliest references to American Negro drinking practices.[32-35] In refuting the myth that slaves were cheerfully acquiescent, Stampp[35] points to the high incidence of both petty and more systematic theft of plantation products, liquor and personal possessions of slaveholders, and claims that the survival of slavery in the Antebellum South depended upon elaborate techniques of slave control, one element of which was the legal denial of unrestricted access to alcoholic beverages and harsh penalties for whites who sold slaves liquor without the owner's permission. Some slaveholders supplied liquor for medicinal purposes, for instance childbirth (Note 34, p. 42), and for occasional festivities and holidays such as at Christmas or for corn shuckings. These celebrations may have been part of the control system, designed to orient slaves toward "prospective pleasures within the limits of slavery" (Note 35, p. 169) and to act as safety valves. A few ritualistic elaborations of these occasions developed—the John Canoe celebration at Christmastime along the Atlantic seaboard (Note 32, p. 198), persimmon parties in Virginia, and sugar cane cutting ceremonies in Louisiana (Note 35, p. 368)—each involving some ceremonial use of alcohol. Stampp stresses however that the dominant function of drinking for slaves was utilitarian, as the "only satisfactory escape from the indignities, the frustrations, the emptiness, the oppressive boredom of slavery" (Note 35, p. 371). As such it involved heavy drinking and intoxication which, though reflecting "an age of hard liquor and heavy drinkers," also had special utility for those enduring slavery. Legal restraints were not very effective in deterring slaves from acquiring liquor. At Christmas, for example, if owners did not provide liquor, slaves took it upon themselves to do so. A former slave recalls that to be sober during the holidays was "disgraceful; and he was esteemed a lazy and improvident man, who could not afford to drink whisky during Christmas" (Note 35, p. 370).

Next chronologically is a study of the relationship of poverty to alcohol use at the end of the nineteenth century.[85] In a chapter devoted to Negro alcohol use a potpourri of data is presented, including ethnographic descriptions of drinking customs prepared expressly for the study by Negroes and (presumably) knowledgeable whites. All data sources are in agreement that for both rural and urban Negroes alcoholism is very rare. Prolonged drinking sprees, continuous drinking at home, and work incapacitation due to drinking are practically unknown.

Descriptions of alcohol use by Negroes in rural areas, where the majority of the Negro population was concentrated, link the use of alcohol to: 1. home celebrations on Christmas day; 2. the observance of Saturday as a day for marketing, idling, and drinking; and 3. where prohibition (most of the agricultural South was under local prohibition at this time) was not in effect, public social gatherings, camp meetings, and other religious gatherings. Intoxication is viewed permissively. The normative orientation toward drinking is distinctly convivial, with much treating and hilarity. Men form stable drinking groups of about six persons who divide a quart bottle of whiskey. The impression of conviviality is reinforced by distinctions made with respect to intoxication. Deep intoxication is not sought: "Many get 'pretty full' but not many 'down drunk'" (Note 85, p. 162). The impact of local prohibition falls more heavily on women than on men. Before prohibition wives and children were taken to the saloon; women drank "more freely." Under prohibition women and children drink less, although "rough women" drink a lot and some of the "better class" take liquor at home or with their husbands on Saturday night. It is not clear whether the amount of female drinking diminished, or only its public visibility. There is some involvement of Negroes in the production and distribution of alcoholic beverages. In remote hill regions where corn is the staple, Negroes often engage in small scale moonshining[86] which is more economically profitable than hauling corn to a distant market.[87] Although unlikely to operate a bar, Negroes monopolize the "walking blind tiger" business, carrying a whiskey flask from which drinks are sold at five cents apiece.

Negro life in southern cities is marked by an increase in male inebriety (or at least it is identified as more of a problem in urban areas). This the writer connects with common features of Negro life in southern cities: poverty, exclusion from skilled labor occupations, and employment practices which encourage economic dependency in the male relatives of female domestics, as well as the ubiquity of the "treating" custom at bars. A relatively high arrest rate for aggressive or disorderly behavior while intoxicated is also noted and "explained" by a curious blend of racial stereotypes and admission of differential police action.

Finally, Negro drinking behavior in northern cities is discussed. A single report, by W. E. B. DuBois for Philadelphia, observes that the Negro population is more socially differentiated than that in southern cities, having a small elite of professionals and proprietors as well as a large laboring class.

DuBois claimed that Negro drinking customs were in the process of transition:[85]

> Drinking among the masses of Negroes is changing from a public to a private custom; from a habit of the excursion, dance and picnic to a habit of home life; from excessive periodic indulgence to a sparing regular partaking; from a use of strong distilled liquors to a use of beer. . . . Excessive use and secret indulgence in liquor is giving place to beer as a table drink or evening beverage, used without concealment of any kind (Note 85, pp. 173–174).

The shift in consumption patterns described by DuBois appears to parallel a comparable trend[88] in the larger culture (Note 88, pp. 3–4). Social class differences were also noted:

> This change has not gone very far as yet, but it is perceptible, and growing among the great mass of working-class Negroes. At the same time, among the better classes and the upper class of working people, all use of liquor in public and in the homes is frowned upon, and is only thus used by older members of the family in secret (Note 85, p. 174).

The contradiction between belief and behavior noted for upper status Negroes is the first documentation of cultural ambivalence regarding alcohol use to appear for any part of Negro society. The Negro church was actively discouraging drinking at this time.

Major works from the 1930s and early 1940s dealing with some aspect of American Negro life[89-96] contain allusions to drinking behavior, but these tend to be scattered references which are not accorded any systematic treatment. Themes suggested in Koren[85] recur regularly, with further elaborations. Prominent among them is the idea that behavior with reference to alcoholic beverages is an explicit criterion for social status placement within the Negro community.

Middle and upper status Negroes, articulate in their rejection of lower class life styles, object especially to those features of lower class Negro drinking felt to reflect on the respectability of the group as a whole—boisterous or indecorous public drinking, drunkenness and drunken fights by both men and women either on the streets or in public drinking establishments. The value upper status groups place on symbolizing their success through conspicuous consumption and display in the context of social associations—still evident in Frazier's[97] description of contemporary value patterns among middle-class Negroes—is another source of differentiation from the lower class person who is less inclined or able to make the drinking situation an occasion for material elaborations and who is more apt to allocate his income on commercial forms of recreation than on voluntary organizations— "he goes behind posts and drinks whisky out of a bottle with a paper bag over it," "hangs out in small, unclean taverns" (Note 92, p. 519) or in socially disesteemed "jook houses" [beer parlors with a juke box (Note 90, p. 225)] and attends "pay parties" (Note 90, p. 225).

Where members of the lower class do join associations, these are apt to be church-related. Lower class churches do not strongly constrain their membership toward middle class behavior models. Lower class church groups are described as dancing and drinking more readily and with less desire to conceal this type of behavior than middle class church groups.[90] Churches may condemn drunkenness, adultery and violence but these "are not preferred subjects for denunciation by the minister" (Note 91, p. 236). Most pronounced in rural areas, but carried over into the urban environment is the pattern of weekend drinking as an integral part of recreation. Saturday as a day for marketing, idling, and drinking still persists.[95] The Saturday night rural "frolic" for younger community members is described by Johnson (Note 95, pp. 180–182) most vividly:

> These affairs begin as dances where refreshments are sold and wind up frequently, in the most wanton merrymaking. In this respect they are characteristic of all peasant merrymaking, a reaction to, and escape from, the other extreme of their life-cycle. The frolics . . . are held from house to house; there is usually an abundance of corn whisky available, and they not infrequently end in violence. The houses are small and ill-lighted and couples make little secret of the character and intensity of their love-making . . .

In the urban environment this recreational pattern revolves around the commercial drinking establishment.

Although alcoholic beverages are used at all social status levels, little is said about middle or upper class Negro drinking. The upper class drinks at cocktail parties and other social gatherings, with preference for status-conferring beverages such as champagne. (Bauer's[98] study of scotch-buying habits of socially mobile Negro males similarly suggests the current symbolic value of beverage choice.) Qualitative differences between middle and upper class drinking behaviors and attitudes are hinted at in *Deep South*.[90] Part of the small upper class is described as attempting to compensate for not being white by considerable indulgence in self-expressive behaviors. The middle class—which also drank, but perhaps more temperately—"regarded the upper class as sexually immoral, as practiced in lewd dancing, card-playing, drinking and smoking . . ." (Note 90, p. 230). A similar theme is suggested in the epilogue to *Black Metropolis* (Note 92, pp. xxvi–xxvii in "Bronzeville, 1961") where anodynes for the effects of segregation and discrimination are listed as: "religion, the social ritual, whisky, dope—and for those who can afford it, an occasional trip to Europe, Latin America, or Africa as a kind of play therapy."

Where there is any ambivalence about drinking, it appears most likely to be centered in the middle class. Abstinence from alcohol is sometimes part of the behavioral constellation accompanying mobility from the lower class or is emphasized as a middle-class virtue.[91] Thus, Hill, studying all-Negro communities in Oklahoma oriented toward proving their autonomy from whites and emphasizing their respectability, notes that "the largest number of ordinances . . . are focused upon the use and sale of alcoholic beverages. Laws prohibiting 'selling, bartering or giving away' intoxicating drinks . . . are numerous. Also, being 'drunk' in public[99] and having 'liquors' on one's person make one liable to immediate arrest" (Note 99, p. 107). Just as mobility into the respectable middle class may be abetted by abstinence, a middle class family's loss of status may begin with "drunkenness or promiscuous sexual behavior by the parents," or ". . . bootlegging or other 'shady' enterprises" (Note 89, p. 156). Sometimes when internal distinctions are made within middle-class church groups with regard to alcohol, these are age-related. Middle-aged groups, who "avoided . . . drinking except in the intimate groups of their fellow members" strongly disapproved the freer dancing, drinking and card-playing of younger middle-status church groups (Note 90, p. 219). Variations in drinking behavior may also be related to position within the middle class. An observer at a social club's business meeting, where lower class persons "on the way up" displayed a blend of lower and middle class behaviors was told "Don't think we carry on like this all the time. . . . You know sometimes we just get a little too much under the belt." The authors comment that "typical middle-class club members in the middle age group don't cut up quite this way at club meetings, even when they 'have too much.' In fact, they wouldn't take too much—at a business meeting" (Note 92, p. 707).

In the mid-1950s an anthropological study of Negro life in a South Carolina mill town appeared, and included a detailed description of contemporary drinking practices[100] and an attempt to relate the use of alcohol to other aspects of the culture.[101] Within the small town of "Kent" (population 4000, one-quarter of whom are Negro), with its composite of rural and urban traditions, Lewis describes the values of the Negro subculture as:

> the accepted and prized values of American culture, survival and getting along; opportunity and equality; patience, religious salvation; self-expression and individuation; inviolability of the ego; friendliness and courtesy; property and money (Note 101, p. 311).

The realities of the local situation are such, however, that conventional means for attaining major ends are often lacking and initiative is discouraged. Adaptations occur therefore and in the process some significant values such as getting along and survival, religious salvation, and inviolability of the ego acquire added emphases and distorted meanings.

Three organizing principles seem to underlie the subculture: the axiom that "white folks is white folks"—this is not only a recognition of a gulf between the groups and differences in power, but it also implies a set of expectations and proscriptions with respect to behavior; the religious myth of salvation—this is the promise of eternal reward at relatively small price and an assurance that "Jesus will make it up to you"; and group self-blame—this latter is a rationalization that has the effect of diverting blame from others, fate, society, etc., and placing it upon one's own people and ways; there is an added implication that personal and group destinies can be self-determined, i.e., improvement will come when the ways are altered or changed. Like other features of the subculture, there is no necessary logical consistency among these elements (Note 101, p. 313).

According to Lewis, social stratification in Kent Negro society is minimal, and the color line and denial of individual respect, rather than internal status rankings, are the sources of frustrations and aggressions. Counterbalancing the conformity and overt passivity in role relationships with whites is a significant emphasis upon self-expression, self-indulgence and release, and patterned nonconformity within the Negro community.

In this cultural context, whiskey drinking assumes considerable significance. Its patterning in terms of sex and social status differentiations is reminiscent of observations reported more than fifty years previous in Koren.[85] Predictably, drinking behavior is one axis along which social distinctions are made. The major status cleavage is in terms of respectability. While whiskey drinking is universal among adult males and very frequent for lower status females, upper status females do not drink or at least do not admit to it except among intimates. Among men, upper status "respectables" confine their drinking to home use in the company of associates. Lower status "nonrespectables" on the other hand have one or more of these characteristics: public drinking with anyone, in taverns or on the street; a reputation for excessive drinking; an arrest record; and nonconventional family life or sexual promiscuity. Bootleggers are included in an elite of the nonrespectables.

Intensive weekend drinking for lower status males is again noted, with the idealized pattern involving purchase of a supply of whiskey at a liquor store, sharing a drink in a semi-public area of the business district, making the rounds of taverns or remaining in a favorite tavern for many hours, and purchasing supplementary whiskey from a bootlegger. Search for a sexual partner is apt to be part of the pattern, although some confine their weekend activity to getting drunk, with an assumed risk of being arrested and fined ten dollars. Drinking is also more prominent during periods of seasonal unemployment, when adult males of all ages join other unemployed males in public idling along the streets of the main business district, in the parking areas behind it, or in the tavern, where groups gather to loaf, drink, argue, and bet on baseball games. In this way the cycle of economic activity contributes to the idling pattern, which includes drinking.

For women, alcohol use is even a more stringent criterion of social status than among men, but circumstances of alcohol use are a factor in social differentiation. The very fact of alcohol use is the differentiator for women. However, sex role differences in alcohol use are much more pronounced for upper than lower status women. This probably reflects a generally greater sex role differentiation in other spheres for the upper status group, and the greater power of upper status males to exact circumspect behavior from upper status females, since these women are also less likely than lower status women to display frank, independent sex interest and promiscuity. Among lower status females, drinking is unlikely to be as extensive as it is for lower status males. Some lower status women do not drink. Virtually all lower status men do. Moreover females do not participate in the daily idling pattern. They do frequent taverns, however, and in comparison to lower status white women in the same community[102] they are much more apt to drink and to be tavern patrons. A type of nonrespectable woman, or "bad woman," is described as extremely indiscreet, loose, unethical and . . . usually a heavy drinker. "She is the female counterpart of the male 'nuisance drunk' in terms of persistence and a certain imperviousness to insult" (Note 101, p. 253).

The tavern is the key locale for public drinking and an important Negro community institution. Focal points of interest and activity are limited to home, job, church, and tavern. Although church and tavern represent the extremes of respectable and nonrespectable behavior, they serve analogous functions: Each is an accepted area for seeking individual recognition and for relatively uncircumscribed behavior, provides a mode of relief from problems, attracts a regular clientele to customary, ritual-like attendance, and is run by and for Negroes. The tavern is characterized as a source of company, excitement and danger, with all parts of Kent Negro society perceiving it as a locale in which the risk of injury is high. Describing his observation of a popular combination grocery-cafe-beer parlor, Lewis notes that it is most heavily patronized on Friday and Saturday, by men and women in the ratio of two to one, and predominantly by persons in their early twenties. Beer and wine are sold, with beer the preferred drink, but patrons also supplement surreptitiously with bootleg whiskey purchased outside the cafe. A juke box and floor space for dancing are provided, and large signs enjoin the patrons against cursing, whiskey drinking, and creating a disturbance. The tavern crowd typically is composed of small groups, with no common focus of attention except for occasional arguments or displays of exhibitionistic dancing.

Since it is an accepted pattern of sociability and sharing, the great bulk of drinking is group drinking. Some informants report lack of enjoyment in lone drinking; others perceive participation in drinking groups as a prerequisite to having friends. Among public drinkers, a bottle tends to be shared by close acquaintances, or by persons who have contributed to its purchase. If a drink is offered to others, it is a gesture of hospitality or good will. At the same time, an underlying tension between inclinations towards friendliness and distrust of others is evident in this practice: The person who owns or offers whiskey, when drinking among casual acquaintances, must himself always take the first drink to allay suspicion.

Whiskey drinking, in this subculture, both contributes to social integration and also figures heavily in disruptive behavior. Although whiskey is not a necessary condition, it frequently accentuates other culturally-instilled tendencies toward touchiness or hypersensitivity to insult or perceived insult, and toward a disposition to violence.[122] Intoxication or drinking ranked first in frequency as a condition under which aggression would occur, according to a content analysis of the field notes for this study (Note 101, p. 209).

Lewis speaks of a "near-successful integration" of whiskey

drinking with other aspects of the culture, pointing to: 1. its pervasiveness; 2. indulgent and tolerant attitudes toward it, except by females who may feel most strongly about its impact on income, status, and personal relations; 3. the frequency with which whiskey is associated with nonmarital sex play, touchy behavior, and "having a good time"; and 4. the lack of elaborate rationalizations for heavy and regular drinking or intoxication. Men seem to view drinking as a personal right and, if borrowing money for whiskey, rarely conceal the purposes of the loan. If alcohol use is thought of as problematic, it is perceived as an individual or family problem rather than as a social problem.

Limits to the extent of integration of drinking with the culture are most apparent from perspectives other than that of lower status males. Alcohol use is, "for many . . . a gesture of defiance to family and community" (Note 101, p. 207). Probably, the most directly felt source of disapproval is from wives and mothers, for whom anxiety over male drinking is common. Across status lines permissiveness regarding drinking is also circumscribed, since respectables do not condone public drinking and release. Finally, in terms of the white community, public drunkenness is an arrestable offense. Although lower status males may see drinking as their right, from their perspective also it entails possibly negative personal consequences. These they attempt to minimize or accept as a calculated risk; in either case some residual tension is likely. Even among nonrespectable drinkers, there are some cultural casualties. There is an internal ranking system of those who are habitually intoxicated in which "sociable" and "nuisance" drunks are distinguished. "The 'nuisance drunk' is looked down upon even by other inveterate drinkers. Lowest in status of those in this group are those who habitually get drunk off cheap wine. In general, nuisance drunks are termed 'crazy'" (Note 101, p. 250). Lastly, in a typology of drinkers Lewis alludes to a type of spasmodic drinker, "the confirmed drinker who has been ill or who has sought to stop but breaks out once in a while in a rash of drinking" (Note 101, p. 205). This description suggests an addictive drinking pattern.

Although recognizing that drinking is an essential feature of social ritual and recreational activity among Kent Negroes, Lewis also emphasizes the personality functions of alcohol for the individual operating within this culture:

. . . it eases personal tensions (while at the same time creating new ones) in a culture that has many "tough" features—status and respect hunger, limited access to rewards, a measure of economic uncertainty. It is also, for many, a temporary ego-booster and a gesture of defiance to family and community. The emphasis upon alcohol as a sort of personal and social "lubricant" suggests the importance of individual release and self-expression as values (Note 101, p. 207).

Given the inconsistencies within the subculture and the indignities imposed by whites in Kent, there is reason to suppose that the utilitarian orientation toward alcohol use would take precedence over the convivial, as is implied above. Yet, evidence to support this assumption is not presented in *Blackways of Kent*. However, nontechnical[103-107] essays (Note 103, p. 41; Note 104, pp. 56–71), fiction (Note 106, pp. 150–153), and poetry (Note 107, pp. 128–129) dealing with contemporary American Negro life also stress the utilitarian aspects of Negro drinking. Straus and Winterbottom's study of domestic servants[105] suggests a somewhat greater prevalence of this orientation among Negro than white female domestics. Negroes were disproportionately represented among those giving individual reasons for their drinking (relaxation, relief of fatigue, forgetting worries).

Summarizing Lewis's contribution to the literature on lower status Negro drinking behavior, use of alcoholic beverages is a prominent feature of life. Alcohol is pervasive in terms of the numbers of males and lower status females who use it, and in terms of its association with recreation, nonmarital sex behavior, and touchy behavior. Intoxication generally is not sanctioned negatively. Alcohol use is one of the axes along which social status is measured in a community whose access to individual recognition and achievement in the larger society is severely limited. Its use reflects some of the important values in the subculture, self-expression and self-indulgence or release. It has utilitarian functions for the personality in a subculture and society generating acute adjustment needs with some frequency. The network of sharing relationships in drinking groups functions to increase social integration; at the same time alcohol use abets social disruption by accentuating tendencies toward touchy behavior and aggression. Finally, in a community where few occupational opportunities are open to Negroes, the distribution of alcoholic beverages either through tavern operation or through bootlegging is a significant means of employment.

From a consideration of drinking behavior and attitudes in Negro communities as a whole we turn to recent studies focusing on youth in particular.[17, 108-112] McReynolds[110] and Sills[111] have surveyed the incidence of drinking among high school students in southern communities, relating this to other social characteristics of these groups. For a random sample of over 500 white and Negro high school students in two Mississippi communities, one "dry" and the other legalizing the use of beer, McReynolds found no significant differences between white and Negro students in incidence or frequency of use. Relatively few students drink (35 percent of the white and 40 percent of the Negro students), and they drink infrequently (only 10 percent of the Negro students drink "frequently," and this designation includes some who drink no more often than once a month!). For both Negroes and whites, those least apt to drink are female; they are of low social status and have few or no friends who drink. Interracial differentials in the areas of education and religion are evident. The proportion of drinkers tends to increase with advancing grade level, but this relationship reverses for the Negro sample in the twelfth grade, suggesting that those who drop out are apt also to be drinkers. Similarly, the frequency of church attendance by white students and by their parents is positively associated with abstaining; for Negro students the relationship is in the same direction but is not significant. This finding is in keeping with our earlier observations on the role of the church vis-a-vis alcohol use in lower class Negro society.

Sills' study[111] of approximately 1500 students in North Carolina Negro high schools,[113] is somewhat less restricted in scope and measures of drinking behavior than that of Mc-

Reynolds. The major instrument for measuring drinking behavior in this study, Mulford and Miller's Quantity-Frequency Index,[6] has since been criticized by Knupfer and Room[114] for obscuring important quantitative differences in drinking behavior. For instance, by its attention to approximate total amount consumed per time unit, "a person who consumes two drinks every day will have the same weekly intake as a person who consumes fourteen drinks every Saturday night, even though the drinking patterns are very different in their social and psychological significance" (Note 114, p. 227). Therefore, Sills' findings are best discussed in terms of a drinking-abstaining dichotomy only. As with Mississippi high school students,[110] abstainers predominated in the North Carolina sample (67 percent). Most drinkers (27 percent) were designated "light drinkers," that is, they drank once a month or less in any amount, and their most used beverage was beer. One fifth of the sample admitted to having been high or tight at least once. Drinking took place most frequently in a private home (56 percent), but 12 percent usually drink in a car; most drink with age peers (68 percent) but 10 percent reported drinking alone. Males were more apt to drink than females (45 vs. 23 percent). The probability of using alcohol increased with advancing age and grade level. Sixty percent of the fathers and only 28 percent of the mothers drink. Maternal drinking behavior was more important than paternal in determining whether the student would drink, but the drinking status of very close friends seemed most influential. These same variables also affected frequency of drinking.

Exposure to inebriety models is not uncommon. Thirteen percent of the students claimed they live with someone who drinks "too much at times," and 70 percent know someone who does. Substantial ambivalence or abstinence indoctrination is suggested by the fact that most of the students (94 percent) stated their parents disapproved the use of alcohol by their children, and 44 percent of the student drinkers disapproved their own drinking. Since the North Carolina sample was almost exclusively of low social status, this finding contrasts sharply with the picture previously drawn by Lewis[101] and others of lower class Negro permissiveness with respect to drinking. It suggests either greater disparity between drinking behavior and values than is usually attributed to the lower class Negro, or that by studying only those Negro youth in high school Sills has introduced a selective bias toward the socially mobile.

Although drinkers and nondrinkers in a subsample ($N = 206$) agreed substantially on most important reasons for which students drink (desire for peer group acceptance, desire to assume an adult-like role) or do not drink (morally wrong, parentally disapproved), drinkers place much more emphasis on the function of alcohol as a relaxer of inhibitions, suggesting a utilitarian component to their orientations even in adolescence.

Variations in the drinking behavior of North Carolina Negro high school students by age, sex, grade in school, and parental drinking behavior, characteristic beverage choice, and reasons for drinking resemble findings for white high school students.[115] The admission by one-third of the students that they drink places them in the lower end of the range noted for other communities in percent of high school student drinkers, and is consistent with the results of a 1949 poll[116] in which regional comparisons showed the percent of student drinkers to be lowest in the South. Given the high drop-out rate of Negro students from high school, however, the drinking behavior of these teen-agers cannot be generalized to all Negro youth in the locality under study. At best it suggests that Negro youth who manage to remain in high school do not differ markedly in their drinking behavior from other high school students.

A very different picture of the drinking habits of lower class Negro youth emerges when studying adolescents in or out of school who live in a midwestern urban center.[112] The data, qualitative in nature, derive from a broad community study of an all-Negro housing project population characterized by poverty, economic dependency, and marital instability. The average annual income is under $2500; over half the families have no male head; and over half receive public assistance. At least two-fifths of the 57 youths studied are currently out of school, most as official drop-outs or chronic truants.

Children in the project grow up in an atmosphere communicating the great salience of drinking through the ubiquitous presence of discarded alcoholic beverage containers around buildings and in children's play areas, the ecological concentration near the project of well-patronized taverns and liquor stores, and a wide array of human role models for consumption of alcohol. Opportunities for project youth to make repeated observations of drinking by adults in their social world, not infrequently their next-of-kin, abound. The public nature of much of this drinking and its consequences makes it possible for children from homes in which there is little or no alcohol use to be almost as familiar as those from homes where alcohol is used liberally with the phenomena of frequent, heavy consumption of alcohol, intoxication, and the association of both enjoyment and trouble with alcohol.

These youth manifest pronounced ease of entry into adult drinking patterns and other behaviors ordinarily the prerogative of adults. The relatively low impact of common agents of childhood socialization—family, school, church, and youth organizations—in either guiding toward specific goals or in diverting or restraining from others, as well as the accelerated entry of lower class Negro youth into adult status and their participation in informal recreation at times with persons many years their senior, appears to be related to early involvement in drinking that cannot be characterized as merely experimental.

The social contexts within which youth in the project learn to drink include "tasting" at home at Christmastime or on other occasions of parental alcohol use, and drinking: 1. with a group of same-sex peers in the home of one of them under the loose supervision or with the participation of a parent; 2. publicly or in an apartment with an unsupervised group of peers of either the same or both sexes; 3. at a "quarter" party where participants pay to attend, may range widely in age and be unknown to one another and the host, and to which they bring their own liquor; and 4. to a lesser extent, at taverns, especially if they are in late adolescence.

Classifying the drinking behavior of 57 boys and girls between the ages of 12 and 20 known to the research staff, few are found to abstain (93 percent drink); sex role variations in drinking-abstaining are negligible (94 percent of males and 91 percent of females drink); and the percentage of drinkers does not show a generally steady increase with age, with those between ages twelve and fourteen as apt to drink as their seniors, again suggesting early entry into drinking. To determine whether these findings are an artifact of non-random sampling or are typical of youth in the project generally would require a more extensive and systematic survey.

Impressionistically, drinking tends to be more intensive than that characterizing American youth generally. The frequency of references to intoxication, easy familiarity with a variety of brands of wine and liquor and spontaneous discussion of brand preferences, and descriptions of quantities of alcohol consumed at given events suggest that much adolescent alcohol use is an approximation of adult consumption patterns.

Distinctive attitudes surround the use of wine. Preference for it is explained in terms of its ability to induce the maximum effect for the minimum amount of money, but its use is associated with low status both because it is "cheapest" in reference to a cost-effects ratio, and especially because its use is connected closely with the disesteemed status of "wino." Adolescent lore further associates the use of wine, especially white port wine, with particularly deleterious physicial and behavioral effects, and an unusual ability to addict. Negative and ambivalent feelings, therefore, attend wine drinking and are reflected in a tendency to deny its very evident use even when other alcoholic beverage use is freely admitted.

The management of the effects of alcohol for adolescent males are apparent in peer group codes surrounding the extent and visibility of intoxication as it relates to protection of the drinker from the potential depredations of others, and the channeling of disruptive concomitants of drinking away from the drinker's family. Effects-management problems for adolescent females revolve around the maintenance of an element of choice in sexual behavior and, for some, a delicate balance in drinking behavior so as to avoid being labeled either "maritally undesirable" or "square."

Analysis of the drinking act suggests that for most project youth studied, the object of drinking is to become "high." It is both an end in itself, subculturally defined as a valued experience, and a means to other desired ends, especially the enhancement of dramatic self-presentation[116] in which the individual seeks to make himself an attractive and interesting object to others so as to win their recognition and better manipulate them. It also furthers social integration in an environment where it is difficult for the individual to achieve a sense of solidarity, trust, and common purpose with others through: 1. organization of activity around the purchase and consumption of alcohol; 2. symbolizing identity and friendship with the peer group by co-participation in a valued activity and by the abandonment of caution and reserve while getting "high" in the presence of others; and 3. facilitating sociability through slight or moderate pharmacologically-induced mood alteration. This integrative function is more significant to all-male than all-female groups, who have other sources of common interest and who are somewhat less likely to engage in constant competitive verbal contests. Drinking also provides an institutional mechanism for the initiation of heterosexual relationships, and is intricately intertwined with sexual behavior. The potential for symbolizing the transformation of adolescent to adult status through the use of alcohol assumes far less importance among project adolescents than has been reported for other American adolescents.[115]

Alcohol use among lower class Negro adolescents in this study can therefore be characterized as highly prevalent, with consumption patterns tending early to approximate those of adults. Becoming "high" is deliberately sought and valued. Drinking orientations are in many ways utilitarian as well as convivial. Although drinking is closely related to other aspects of the culture, some ambivalence is observed around the use of wine and on the part of girls attempting to reconcile conflicting expectations with respect to female drinking. The drinking behavior of lower class adolescents in this midwestern urban center has much in common with that observed by Lewis[101] among lower class Negroes in a small southern town.

Turning from lower status adolescents to middle status college students, Straus and Bacon's[17] study of the drinking behavior of 15,700 students at 27 colleges included data from two southern colleges for Negroes and one northern college with a sizeable Negro enrollment. Regional differences between these two groups (if any) are unreported, as is the size of the Negro sample. Findings for the Negro student group as a whole reflect a greater prevalence of drinking than is reported for southern Negro high school students,[110, 111] and a lower prevalence than that reported for lower class midwestern adolescent Negroes:[112] 81 percent of males and 43 percent of females use alcohol. The discrepancy between the sexes in prevalence of drinking is larger than that reported for any other ethnic group of college students (Note 17, p. 53), and is reminiscent of Lewis's[101] observation for Negroes in a southern town that sex role differentiation in drinking behavior among "respectables" is considerable. Compared to other ethnic groups, Negro college students also rank low in incidence of drinkers. For males of nine ethnic groups, only "Americans" (whites whose family has been in the United States for at least three generations) report a lower percentage of drinkers; for females, Negroes rank lowest in percent of alcohol users.

Lastly, in two studies of Negro male undergraduates at small, church-related colleges in the deep South, Maddox and Allen[108] and Maddox and Borinski[109] have explored the meanings attached to alcohol use. In the first of these[108] an analysis of the responses of 24 male volunteers to a modified form of the TAT revealed that: 1. Alcohol is perceived predominantly as an instrument of reality modification as opposed to convivial social interaction. In 75 percent of the stories given, the use of alcohol was associated with anxiety reduction, sexual stimulation or seduction, or compensation for personal or social inadequacies. 2. The consequences of drinking are perceived as negative, in terms of conventional notions of propriety or morality. In 70 percent of the specified consequences, drinking was linked to inebriety, physical aggression, seduction, alcohol addiction, and severance of family relationships. 3. There was little elaboration of either the situational factors associated with drinking, such as time, place, and occasion, or of the social characteristics of users, other than their sex (usually male). 4. Fantasy characters tended to make negative judgments of drinking, as inappropriate or morally wrong.

Comparing these results with a parallel study of 24 white students' fantasies about alcohol,[118] Maddox and Allen found no significant differences between them in tendency to associate negative consequences with drinking or in identifying alcohol primarily as functional for reality modification, although Negro students exhibited a more intense form of the utilitarian orientation toward alcohol. Negroes were significantly more likely than whites to attribute negative judgments of drinking to their fantasy characters, and less likely to elaborate the situational factors of use or social characteristics of users. When interviewed about their drinking behavior, they also showed significantly more ambivalence: two-thirds of the Negro students who prefer to be identified by their peers as nondrinkers had had current and regular drinking experience ($N = 15$); only one-fourth of white students who prefer the non-drinker designation were actually drinkers ($N = 12$). Findings regarding the negative and ambivalent orientation of the Negro sample toward alcohol are interpreted in light of Frazier's[97] description of the ambiguous social position of the "black bourgeoisie," their acceptance wholesale of the values and moral codes of middle-status whites, and the impact of the puritanical morality they encounter in the church-related colleges. Frazier is cited regarding the use of alcohol in "narcotizing" doses to cope with feelings of inferiority and frustration. Maddox and Allen conclude that: "The observed ambivalence is a product of folk culture, in which alcohol is not a clearly defined social object, encountering the 'missionary piety' or distinctive ethic the middle-status white applies to drinking," (Note 108, p. 426).

In a later study of Negro male collegians[109] Maddox and Borinski pursue further the middle-status Negro's perceptions and use of alcohol, hypothesizing that: 1. In any population of Negro males, drinking will be prevalent; 2. The incidence of complications associated with drinking will be high; and 3. If the males are identified with or aspire to middle status, the complications found will include indications of self-disparagement in part explained by their drinking.

A probability sample of 50, representing one-fourth of the male students at the studied institution, was interviewed. It was established that they were of middle status, and that there was presumptive evidence of their exposure to a Protestant version of middle-status moral standards or of willingness to expose themselves to this tradition. Drinking was indeed prevalent, with nine out of ten students reporting some current drinking, a higher proportion than had been found by Straus and Bacon[17] for comparable groups. However, in terms of quantity and frequency[119] more Negro students were light drinkers (55 percent) than had been reported for Iowans[6] of comparable age (30 percent), education (41 percent), or religion (47 percent), or for Protestant college students[17] (42 percent).

Although they had not experienced intoxication and problems as a result of drinking more frequently than other college students, the drinking style of these students was characterized by an unusually high preoccupation with alcohol, as measured by a scale of items describing drinking behaviors frequently affirmed by alcoholics.[120] Furthermore, the meanings attached to alcohol use were again shown to be utilitarian and negative in orientation. On a scale designed to assess drinking motives,[121] 59 percent of Negro collegians (as contrasted with 30 percent of male Iowans) defined alcohol in terms of its use for personal effect. Similar orientations were elicited with a modified form of the TAT and a semantic differential test as well.

Despite the fact that most of these students drank, many had been exposed to parentally negative attitudes towards drinking. Sixty-three percent had been advised by adults, primarily their parents, to abstain. A majority of students who described both parents as non-users and all who indicated that one parent only drank, were themselves users of alcohol.

The study concludes with a test of evidence tending to

support Lemert's (Note 19, p. 366) contention that persons
exposed to the Protestant Ethic drink at the expense of self-
esteem. Self-esteem, as measured by statements in which the
student might describe himself in disparaging terms or attribute disparaging statements about him to others, showed
an inverse relationship with drinking, the quantity-frequency
of alcohol consumption, the definition of alcohol in terms of
personal effects, and preoccupation with its use.

In reviewing studies of or allusions to American Negro
drinking behavior, one finds few generalizations emerging that
can adequately characterize the drinking behavior of this
ethnic group as a whole, owing to the pronounced cleavage in
life style between lower status Negroes and those above them.
The clearest variations in alcohol use by socio-economic status
occur in the choice of public vs. private locales for drinking,
elaboration of the drinking ritual and attention to the symbolic value of alcoholic beverages, and permissible behavior
accompanying drinking—especially in regard to aggression.

Where the entire Negro community has been studied, systematic and quantified alcohol-use data are lacking; where
data meeting these specifications are available, they pertain
to small, select populations whose characteristics exclude the
great mass of American Negroes. Therefore on the basis of
research conducted to date, we cannot generalize from a firm
basis of fact regarding the prevalence of drinking and abstaining, or the distribution of drinker types (in terms of quantity
and frequency) by age, sex, social status levels, urban-rural
and regional residence, no less among persons with specified
combinations of these characteristics. Similarly, while utilitarian and to a lesser extent convivial orientations are observed at all levels, their relative distribution by social status
level and other social characteristics is unknown. We need to
check further our impression that drunkenness is not an occasion for negative self-definition by Negroes of lower and
perhaps upper status, but that it may be for those of or
aspiring to middle status. Despite its integration with other
aspects of social life, ambivalence about drinking is manifested
by Negroes of middle and some of lower status. It is not clear
whether this ambivalence can be attributed to a common experience on the part of both, or results for the former from

exposure to conflicting value systems and for the latter from exposure to high rates of trouble associated with drinking. We will need the answer to these and many more questions before we can improve our understanding of the social factors affecting the rates of alcoholism, problem drinking, and alcohol-related offenses for this American ethnic group.

7

The Chronic Drunkenness Offender

DAVID J. PITTMAN, C. WAYNE GORDON

This research report is based upon an analysis of 187 case studies of a random sample of all men who had been sentenced at least twice to a penal institution in New York State on a charge of public intoxication and who were incarcerated in the county jail when the investigation was conducted. Some of the chronic inebriates are confirmed alcoholics; others are miscreants whose present use of alcohol is preliminary to confirmed alcoholism; and others are non-addicted excessive drinkers who will never become alcoholics. This research, then, is concerned with a group of excessive drinkers who may or may not be alcoholics, but whose drinking has involved them in difficulties with the police, the courts, and penal institutions. *They are a group for whom the penal sanctions of the society have failed along with existent community resources for rehabilitation.*

REPRINTED with permission of Rutgers Center of Alcohol Studies.
This article is a summary of the major findings of the book, David J. Pittman and C. Wayne Gordon, *Revolving Door: A Study of the Chronic Police Case Inebriate*, Glencoe, Ill.: The Free Press; and New Brunswick, N. J.: Rutgers Center of Alcohol Studies, 1958.

The extensive case histories of the chronic intoxication offenders may be analyzed in terms of three major sets of factors which are crucial for the development of career patterns in public intoxication. These are: (1) sociocultural determinants; (2) socialization determinants; and (3) alcohol as the adaptive or adjustive mechanism in the life career.

SOCIOCULTURAL DETERMINANTS

The chronic police case inebriate category consists of individuals with definable sociocultural traits as age, nationality background, race, marital status, religion, educational attainment, occupational skills, and previous criminal record.

Age is one of the crucial attributes that differentiates these men from all other offender groups. Their age curve is skewed toward middleage brackets, whereas commitments for such offenses as automobile theft, robbery, and burglary chiefly involve individuals under age 25. Their mean age of 47.7 years and their median age of 48.5 years are higher than those of the general male population, of arrested inebriates, and of patients seen in the alcoholism clinics. This sample is one of the oldest problem drinking groups to be studied, in that 45 per cent are over 50 years of age.

This sample is marked by a high proportion of Negroes (18 per cent) in comparison to their representation in the general population of the county in which the jail is located (2 per cent). Negro and white offenders are marked by age differentials: Two-thirds of the Negroes are under 45 years of age, compared to 30 per cent of the whites. The Negroes are primarily from a rural or small town Southern lower-class background who are having severe difficulties adjusting to the Northern urban pattern.

The most frequently represented nationality groupings are English and Irish. Irish ethnics compose 35 per cent of the sample, but there is an increasing number of Irish with advancing age, especially after 45. Italians, although represented in significant number in the county's general population, compose only 2 per cent of the sample.

In the related area of religious affiliation, the sample consisted of 42 per cent Protestants, 40 per cent Catholics, and 18 per cent who professed no affiliation. There were no Jews. Religion, except in the case of groups such as the Jews who exhibit a specific culture pattern, appears less important as an identifying sociocultural determinant of inebriation than nationality or ethnic status.

The current marital status of these men is one of their most important attributes. Forty-one per cent never married, 32 per cent are separated, 19 per cent are divorced, 6 per cent widowed and 2 per cent were living with their spouses before the current incarceration. Thus for these offenders, 96 per cent of those who had ever married reported broken marriages, whereas the expectancy is only 11 per cent, using the general male population of the county, corrected for age disparities, as the control.

The relationship which exists between marriage stability and problem drinking is a complex one. Many persons do not possess the competences in interpersonal relationships or in personality traits that are associated with entrance into marriage; or, once involved in marriage, these individuals do not possess requisite skills for continuing the marriage. Excessive drinking, which eventually causes severe disruptions in the individual's life, is destructive of the marriage relationship itself.

On the whole, these offenders are an educationally disadvantaged group. Seventy per cent of the sample did not go beyond the eighth grade of school as compared to 40 per cent of the county's general population. This educational impoverishment is reflected in their low order of primary occupational skills. Sixty-eight per cent are unskilled workers, mainly laborers, 22 per cent skilled workers, and 3 per cent professional and allied workers, compared to 13, 46, and 22 per cent, in the respective categories, in the general population.

Experience with the legal process in terms of arrests and incarcerations is another determinant of the career pattern in public intoxication. As a group, the inebriates exhibited a wide variety of criminal histories. The mean number of arrests for all causes is 16.5; the median is 10.2. For public intoxication only, the mean number of arrests is 12.8 and the median is 6.0. The "average" chronic drunkenness offender has experienced some 10 arrests on all charges, and the offender with 30, 40, or more arrests is atypical, though composing a sizable portion of the total.

The sample can be divided into three subgroups by previous criminal record: (a) 31 per cent who had been arrested only for public intoxication; (b) 32 per cent who had been arrested, in addition, on charges probably related to the excessive use of alcohol; and (c) 37 per cent who had been involved in serious violations such as homicide, rape, robbery, or burglary. Men in the latter group showed a tendency to abandon the criminal career after the age of 33 or 40 with an intensified pattern of public intoxication thereafter.

Institutionalized living of the type noted by Straus and McCarthy[1] is a typical pattern of selective adaptation among the chronic police case inebriates. Tendencies toward dependency inherent in the experience of childhood, youth, and early adulthood are reinforced and supported through a selective adaptation to life in the semi-protective environments of the Civilian Conservation Corps, the Army, the railroad gang, the lake steamer, the jail, lumber and fruit camps, hospitals, Salvation Army and kindred shelters. The minimum requirements for living are met through institutional organizations which relieve the incumbents of individual responsibility to cope with food, housing, and related needs. They become habituated to dependent living which further limits their capacity to re-establish independent modes of life.

In summary, lower-class individuals of Irish ethnic status and Negroes in the age bracket 40–49 with previous extensive arrest histories are most vulnerable to repeated arrests for drunkenness.

SOCIALIZATION DETERMINANTS

Within this framework of sociocultural determinants are a series of socialization experiences which are conducive to the development of a career pattern in inebriation. The structural continuity of the family units was broken by death, divorce, or separation before the inebriate's fifteenth birthday in 39 per cent of the cases. This seems to be an extremely high percentage of families whose structure collapsed.

On a more qualitative level, mother-son and father-son relationships evidenced a trend in the direction of serious deprivations for the inebriates in meeting their basic emotional, social, and psychological needs. Thus, the sense of belongingness achieved by membership and acceptance in a social unit larger than the individual himself, such as the family primary group, was only partially attained by most of the inebriates.

An objective index to evaluate adolescent socialization experience and the significance of these situations for positive identity formation was constructed by the following criteria: (a) participation in a clique or close friendship group of boys, (b) heterosexual participation as reflected in an established dating pattern, (c) existence of goals and aspirations, whether middle-class nature or not, (d) family integration as reflected in the individual's sense of belonging to the family unit, and (e) positive school adaptation as reflected in attendance and performance. If all these factors were found in a case, the socialization experience was scored as good or above average; four present was scored adequate or average, and three or fewer was rated as poor or below what would be desired for adequate socialization. The results of these classifications indicated that the symptoms which warn of difficulties in assuming adult social roles are already present in these men at the end of the adolescent development era. By the index of the adolescent adjustment, 86 per cent of our sample was rated poor; only 10 per cent could be rated adequate or average, while in 4 per cent the index could not be applied because of incomplete data. In only one case were all five factors present.

Thus, the chronic police case inebriates are undersocialized, as determined by other quantitative and qualitative indexes for their original families and the adolescent sphere of development. This deficit is reflected in the adult inebriate career in his inability to perform two of the most demanding secondary task roles, i.e., occupational and marital roles.

ALCOHOL AS THE ADJUSTIVE
MECHANISM IN THE LIFE CAREER

The career of the chronic drunkenness offender is one in
which drinking serves the socially handicapped individuals
as a means of adapting to life conditions which are otherwise
harsh, insecure, unrewarding, and unproductive of the es-
sentials of human dignity. This type of career is, however, only
one of the possible patterns of adjustment, given the combination of conditions in the early life of these men. Repeated incarceration for drunkenness is the terminal phase of
a complex process in which the interplay of sociocultural and
personality factors have combined to produce this long-run
adaptation.

Using the age at which a man was committed the second
time for public intoxication or a drinking-involved offense
as a breakpoint, the study group falls into two types which
we shall designate the *Early Skid* and the *Late Skid* careers.

The Early Skid career pattern involves approximately 50
per cent of the offenders. In this group two-fifths of the men
experienced their second incarceration in their twenties and
the rest in their early thirties. Only a few had their second
imprisonment in the age period 36–39.

The Early Skid career pattern is thus one in which the individual establishes his record of public intoxication in his
twenties or early thirties. It represents serious social and/or
psychiatric maladjustment to early adulthood which extends
into middle adulthood. There is an absence of adult occupational adjustment independent of institutional living. The
period of alcohol dependency formation is not associated with
such stable marital adjustment as may be found in some of
the Late Skid career patterns.

The Late Skid career pattern is defined by the postpone-
ment of the minimum record of two incarcerations for public
intoxication until the forties or even fifties. The career type
encompasses 50 per cent of the men in the group if the age 37
(for experiencing the second arrest) is used as the dividing
point.

The period of alcohol dependency development is often marked by extended periods of occupational and family stability. Since this period is accompanied by drinking, it must be regarded as part of the conditioning period of alcohol dependency. More apparent in the Late Skid career is the physical decline of the man who is having great difficulty in maintaining his economic needs through marginal types of employment. Younger men replace him on the casual day-labor jobs. His drinking increases and finally his tolerance for alcohol declines.

In summary, the Early Skid career pattern is one in which drinking serves as the primary means of adjustment to original social and/or psychiatric disability; whereas the Late Skid career pattern is secondary to failure in secondary role performance.

This study has shown the chronic drunkenness offender to be the product of a limited social environment and a man who has never attained more than a minimum of integration in society. He is and has always been at the bottom of the social and economic ladder: he is isolated, uprooted, unattached, disorganized, demoralized, and homeless, and it is in this context that he drinks to excess. As such, admittedly through his own behavior, he is the least respected member of the community, and his treatment by the community has at best been negative and expedient. He has never attained, or has lost, the necessary respect and sense of human dignity on which any successful program of treatment and rehabilitation must be based. He is captive in a sequence of lack or loss of self-esteem producing behavior which causes him to be further disesteemed. Unless this cycle is partially reversed, positive results in treatment will be difficult to attain.

8

Social Policy as
Deviancy Reinforcement:
The Case of the Public
Intoxication Offender

DAVID J. PITTMAN, DUFF G. GILLESPIE

INTRODUCTION

Over the past decade there has been an increasing interest in deviant behavior which has borne fruit in the more precise application to deviance of a number of broader conceptual models—particularly those of structural-functionalism (Parsons, Merton), symbolic interaction (Sutherland, Becker, Goffman), social exchange theory (Homans, Gouldner), and personality models (Cohen, Erikson), as well as development of certain specialized paradigms—e.g., opportunity models (Cloward and Ohlin), subcultural models (Miller), group process models (Short and Strodbeck), and social policy and legal models (Schur, Matza).

PAPER presented at meetings of American Society of Criminology, Berkeley, California, December 28–30, 1965.

The materials for this article have been drawn freely from the senior author's previously published studies and lectures. See: David J. Pittman and C. Wayne Gordon, *Revolving Door: A Study of the Chronic Police Case Inebriate,* Glencoe, Ill., Free Press; and New Brunswick, New Jersey, Rutgers Center of Alcohol Studies, 1958; David J. Pittman and C. Wayne Gordon, "Criminal Careers of the Chronic Police Case Inebriate," *Quart. J. Stud. Alc.,* 19:255–268, June, 1958, republished with minor change as "Criminal Careers of the Chronic Drunkenness Offender," in David J. Pittman and Charles R. Snyder (eds.), *Society, Culture, and Drinking Patterns,* New York: John Wiley and Sons, pp. 535–546; David J. Pittman, "Other Alcoholism Related Problems: Skid Row and the Chronic Drunkenness Offender,"

In this article we will employ a social policy model toward deviancy, drawing on the previous work of Lindesmith, Lemert, Matza and Schur. Our major thesis is that social and legal policies directed toward the resolution or amelioration of a particular deviancy may in effect have the opposite result —namely, the reinforcement of the deviancy and, possibly, resulting secondary deviant acts. This can be illustrated with the phenomena of drug addiction, homosexuality, gambling, "obscene" literature, illegitimacy, and public intoxication. The latter deviancy, exemplified by the chronic police case inebriate, is chosen for analysis in this paper.

DEVIANCY REINFORCEMENT CYCLE

Chart 1 presents the model of the "Deviancy Reinforcement Cycle" which theoretically illustrates sequentially how deviant behavior becomes an object of social policy. "A" on the chart represents the antecedent conditions which are associated with "prodromal behavior" at "B." Although "A" is the etiological source of "B," we are not concerned with causation in this paper. Our contention is that some social problems result from the manner in which society attempts to cope with certain

in Basic Papers from the first Southeastern School of Alcohol Studies, Millsaps College, Jackson, Mississippi, August 6–11, 1961, pp. 92–98; David J. Pittman and Muriel W. Sterne, *Alcoholism: Community Agency Attitudes and Their Impact on Treatment Services,* Washington, D.C.: U.S. Dept. of Health, Education, and Welfare, PHS, Publication No. 1273, 1965; David J. Pittman, "The Chronic Court and Police Case Inebriate," presented at the conference, "The Alcoholic and the Court," sponsored by the Oregon State Board of Control, Gearhart, Oregon, May 23–25, 1963, and also presented, as well as the paper, "So What," at the Southeastern Conference Workshop, "The Chronic Alcoholic Jail Offender," sponsored by the South Carolina Dept. of Mental Health, Charleston, October 28–30, 1964; David J. Pittman, "Social Pathology, Urban Renewal, and the Homeless Man," paper presented at the American Psychological Assn. meetings, St. Louis, 1962, and published in North Carolina, *Inventory,* 12:19–24, 1963, and Alberta, Canada, *Progress,* 4:3–9, 1963; David J. Pittman, "Homeless Men," *Transaction,* January, 1964, pp. 15–16; David J. Pittman, "The Chronic Inebriate: An Overview," in Conference Proceedings "The Court and the Chronic Inebriate," sponsored by the Dept. of Health, Education, and Welfare, Washington, D.C., April 23, 1965.

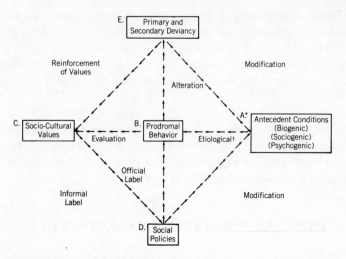

*Letters indicate theoretical sequence of events.
†Arrows indicate theoretical direction of influence.

CHART 1.   Model of the Deviancy Reinforcement Cycle.

behavior whose causes may be unknown, and that these social problems can be greatly alleviated by altering social policies. "Prodromal Behavior" does not become deviant until processes take place "by which persons come to be defined as deviant by others."[1]

This definition of deviancy is the result of socio-cultural values which change through time and space. Ruth Benedict's statement illustrates how one type of behavior may be evaluated by various cultures (represented by "C" on Chart 1) with differing socio-cultural values.

A tendency toward this trait [homosexuality] in our culture exposes an individual to all the conflicts to which all aberrants are always exposed, and we tend to identify the consequences of this conflict with homosexuality. But these consequences are obviously local and cultural. Homosexuals in many societies are not incompetent, but they may be such if the culture asks adjustments of them that would strain any man's vitality. Wherever homosexuality has been given an honorable place in any society, those to whom it is congenial have filled adequately the honorable roles society assigns to them. Plato's *Republic* is, of course, the most convincing statement of such a reading of homosexuality.[2]

All behavior is informally evaluated by society; this evaluation may be positive, neutral, or negative. Deviant behavior (behavior evaluated negatively) can be seen as a breach of mores which invokes informal sanctions on the deviant. For example, illegitimate children may frequently experience informal sanctions, even though illegitimacy is not unlawful.

When the degree and predominance of the negativism of socio-cultural values toward a behavior is intense enough, the informal labeling and sanctions become formal labeling and sanctions. (This is the relationship "C"–"D" on Chart 1.) Matza states, "In democratic societies there has usually been an approximation of consensus on the view that law in some sense ought to reflect community standards."[3] Of course, laws do not always reflect the dominant values of the society. Many laws are archaic, and though at one time they may have represented a dominant socio-cultural value, now they are legal vestiges. For example, often under the generic term of sodomy, most states outlaw oral-genital contacts and other commonly practiced sexual behavior. Too, laws may be the result of the pressures exerted by a small minority rather than a consensus, e.g., "blue-laws" which many communities have. Other laws may represent the consensus of perhaps a majority, but are opposed by a large portion of the population, e.g., the gambling laws of some states. If the public considers a law to be unjust, pressure may be exerted to abolish it; the repeal of Prohibition is an example of such pressure. However, most laws do not affect all segments of the society with such force as Prohibition did. What usually happens is that the enforcers of social policies (the police and courts represented as "D" on Chart 1) become ambivalent in their enforcement because the public ("C" on Chart 1) is essentially indifferent towards this particular form of deviance. However, laws do not have to be enforced rigidly and frequently in order to seriously affect deviant behavior. For example, because of the fact homosexual acts are difficult to detect, the obvious lack of victims to file complaints, and the ambivalence (relative to other deviant behavior) of the larger society, most law enforcement agencies leave homosexual gathering places alone. Still, the fact that there are laws against adult homosexual acts in all

but one of the states (Illinois) has serious effects on homosexuals. As Schur states:

> The homosexual, although the danger of direct police action is
> not overwhelming, must be constantly aware of his precarious posi-
> tion vis-a-vis the law, and of the fact that he himself has little
> resource to the law should such need arise. As a result, he finds
> himself highly vulnerable to exploitation, by the police as well as
> by others.[4]

However, for the homosexual who is definitely committed to
the "gay" life (as opposed to ambisexual individuals), the
effect of social policy is more profound. Lemert states:

> . . . if the deviant acts are repetitive and have a high visibility,
> and if there is a severe societal reaction, which, through a process
> of identification is incorporated as part of the "me" of the indi-
> vidual, the probability is greatly increased that the integration of
> existing roles will be disrupted and that reorganization based upon
> a new role or roles will occur. (The "me" in this context is simply
> the subjective aspect of the societal reaction.)[5]

"Severe societal reaction," in this case, is manifested in
"social policies" ("D" on Chart 1) which alter the role of the
homosexual ("B" on Chart 1) to one that is in obvious conflict
with the mores and laws of the larger society ("E" on Chart
1). Too, the "reciprocal relationship between the deviation of
the individual and the societal reaction" gives rise to an "in-
grouping and outgrouping between society and the deviant."[5]
In this outgroup, the homosexual, in effect, becomes a marginal member of the larger society. This marginal role has
been defined by social policies ("D" → "A" on Chart 1), and
members of the outgroup socialize new members to the
societal role given them ("E" → "A" on Chart 1).

The more intense the enforcement of laws, the greater effect
they have on the deviancy. This can be illustrated by the case
of drug addicts in America. Even though they may never have
personal contact with law enforcement agencies, addicts cannot help but be constantly aware of the law's presence. The
secretive manner in which they must purchase drugs is the
product of law enforcement. Many of their associates (fellow
addicts and pushers) have had personal contact with the law.
Finally, the high price and low quality of the black market

drugs are a result of social policies. The stringent enforcement of narcotic laws produces secondary deviancies among drug addicts ("E" on Chart 1). The addict must resort to illegal behavior to support his habit, usually petty larceny and prostitution. Specifically, Lemert states that "when a person begins to employ his deviant behavior or a role based upon it as a means of defense, attack, or adjustment to the overt and covert problems created by the consequent societal reaction to him, his deviation is secondary."[5] This image of the drug addict as a thief, "whore," and often (unjustly) as a sexual pervert reinforces the societal stereotype of the addict (Relationship "E" → "C" on Chart 1). Yet, there is nothing inherent in drug addiction that forces the addict to commit crimes. In a pilot study of British addicts in London, a number of them were interviewed who had never resorted to criminal activity to support their addiction.[6] Most of these addicts were able to maintain a productive role in society. This is not to say that the "British system" is the answer to America's drug problem, for the socio-cultural values and social policies governing the treatment of the addict are different in England than America.

Using a heuristic model, we have shown how socio-cultural values negatively label behavior and how this evaluation is manifested in social policies. These social policies result in secondary deviancy which are not intrinsic to the original behavior. This secondary deviancy reinforces the larger society's preconceived stereotype of the behavior. Also, social policies influence the socio-cultural context in which deviant behavior develops. Finally, deviant individuals affect the antecedent conditions of behavior by socializing persons to deviant roles. In the following section we will discuss in greater detail this Deviancy Reinforcement Cycle for public intoxication and illustrate how the cycle may be broken.

DEVIANCY REINFORCEMENT CYCLE FOR PUBLIC INTOXICATION

In this section we shall discuss the operation of the deviancy reinforcement cycle for one type of deviant behavior, namely, repeated public intoxication which is a violation of law in American states and municipalities. These chronic drunkenness offenders are a group of excessive drinkers who may or may not be alcoholics, but whose drinking has involved them in difficulties with the police, the courts, and penal institutions. They are a group for whom the penal sanctions of the society have failed along with existent community resources for rehabilitation. Although some of these men (very seldom women) are confirmed alcoholics, others are miscreants whose present use of alcohol is preliminary to confirmed alcoholism, and others are nonaddicted excessive drinkers who will never become alcoholics.

As in the cases of drug addiction and homosexuality, the etiology of alcoholism is unknown. There is the widely held contention that all three conditions are diseases, and the courts, and most legislatures, appear to have accepted this notion for it is not illegal to be a drug addict, homosexual, or alcoholic. Rather, behaviors associated with these diseases are illegal: for the drug addict, it is the illegal procurement, possession, or use of illegal drugs; for the homosexual (with the exception of Illinois), it is homosexual acts of almost any nature; and for the alcoholic, it is public intoxication. Currently, there is concern over whether a person can be arrested for behavior which is a manifestation of a disease. It is felt that such individuals lack *mens rea* or criminal intent, and that ". . . any disease which deprives the individual of capacity to control his conduct will excuse conduct which would otherwise be condemned."[7]

For the chronic alcoholic, this argument is briefly summarized in the following two questions, which to date have not been answered by the courts:

1. Does criminal punishment of a chronic alcoholic for violating a public intoxication statute, when he was powerless to avoid violating that statute, violate the Eighth Amendment of the United States Constitution?
2. Does criminal punishment of a chronic alcoholic, who is a sick person suffering from a disease, merely for publicly exhibiting the symptoms of that sickness and disease, violate the Eighth Amendment of the United States Constitution?[8]

These are very important questions and ones that should be answered, hopefully in favor of the chronic alcoholic. However, there are several reasons why we do not choose this approach. One obvious reason is that, as sociologists, we are not fully qualified to discuss the legal aspects raised in the above issues. But, perhaps more important, such questions deal only with the chronic alcoholic and one manifestation of his disease—public intoxication. Such limitations are shown in the following statement from *Dewitt Easter v. District of Columbia.*

There is no quarrel here with the principle of the *Harris* case that Section 25–128 of the D.C. Code [public intoxication statute] may be used to punish the normal individual who goes on a "binge" from time to time, or the common drunkard whose intoxication results from indolence but not from addiction. Such persons could if they wished, control their drinking, and therefore are criminally responsible for their actions. Nor does Appellant [Easter] argue that a chronic alcoholic who drives a car, or commits murder, is *ipso facto* not guilty. A finding that a chronic alcoholic has no capacity to avoid appearing in public in an intoxicated condition is *not* a finding that a chronic alcoholic may with impunity commit murder . . . that is an entirely different question of criminal responsibility . . . (Note 7, pp. 11–12).

Thus, the *mens rea* approach is aimed at helping only the chronic alcoholic, which does not encompass all chronic drunkenness offenders and does not cope with the great range of alcohol-related offenses, such as vagrancy, common assault, and disorderly conduct. In short, the *mens rea* approach deals with only one aspect, an important one, of the chronic drunkenness offender problem. We are also concerned with "the normal individual who goes on a 'binge' from time to time," and "the common drunkard whose intoxication results from indolence," who, through repeated arrests and incarcerations, are caught up in a deviancy reinforcement cycle that, in effect, is a revolving door; this revolving door may actually contribute to an excessive drinker's becoming an alcoholic and also encourage the public inebriate to act out secondary deviances.

On the whole, Americans have a relatively tolerant orientation toward the drinking of alcoholic beverages as long as one does not drink to excess. Yet, this is not quite true. On certain prescribed occasions it is permissible to drink, not necessarily to the point of intoxication but at least enough to get "high." These occasions are usually private or semiprivate, and range from fraternity "beer blasts" and debutante "coming-out parties" to office parties and conventions. However, when a person's drinking starts to interfere with his work or family life, certain negative sanctions are involved by his friends. His wife may be ashamed to invite guests home, and, correspondingly, friends may be embarrassed to visit. The alcoholic, as Jellinek has pointed out, "begins to drink in private . . . to conceal his drinking problem." But Jellinek was describing the middle-class alcoholic. A middle-class alcoholic, as well as an excessive drinker in this class, is unlikely to come in contact with law enforcement agencies since his behavior is concealed. Too, the public is more likely to view him as an unfortunate, as someone who has a disease and as someone who should seek medical help, although these attitudes are intertwined with moralistic sentiments. Although the public labels these deviant middle-class drinkers negatively, they do not invoke the same harsh sanctions as is true with the lower-class alcoholics. On the other hand, the same public considers lower-class alcoholics and excessive drinkers as derelicts, beggars, petty thieves, and worthless drunks unable to support themselves. One could become indignant and stand up for these lower-class individuals and contend that they are not vagrants, jobless, and so forth, but unfortunately they are. Most of us would agree that it is highly undesirable to have men sleeping in alleys and doorways, breaking into shops and parked cars, and panhandling passersby for a dime or quarter. However, frequently the solution is too simplistic, namely, get them off the streets—put them in jail. Yet the public's negative stereotype of the public intoxication offender is a result of these very punitive policies.

Earlier it was stated that ". . . the more intense the enforcement of laws, the greater the effect they have on the deviancy." For the public intoxication offender, the enforcement is indeed intense. In 1964, the F.B.I. reported 1,458,821 arrests for public drunkenness by 3,977 agencies covering a population of 132,439,000. This figure accounted for over 31 percent of the total arrests for all offenses and is almost twice the number of arrests for Index Crime Offenses. If we included alcohol-related offenses (driving under the influence of alcohol, disorderly conduct, and vagrancy) in this percentage, it would constitute 48.9 percent of all reported arrests.[9] A large number of these actions involve the repeated arrest of the same men. To illustrate, let us take the case of Portland, Oregon, for 1963; in this year there were 11,000 law violations involving drunkenness or the effects of drinking, but only around 2,000 different persons accounted for these arrests.[10]

Too, persons arrested and held for prosecution for public drunkenness are almost always found guilty. In 1964, 1,751 cities, representing a population of 58,915,000, reported to the F.B.I. that 89.4 percent of all persons charged with public drunkenness were found guilty. The next highest percentage was 80.4 percent, and this was for the alcohol-related offense of vagrancy (Note 9, p. 102). These data suggest that the chronic drunkenness offender frequently finds himself incarcerated. Indeed, there is strong evidence that chronic inebriates constitute one of the largest groupings of individuals incarcerated in short-term correctional institutions. Alcohol-related offenses accounted for 35 percent of the incarcerations to the St. Louis City Workhouse for the period, 1957–1959. Benz recently completed a study, *Man on the Periphery*,[11] of the penal population in the Monroe County (Rochester, New York) Jail which showed that alcohol offenders accounted for 62.5 percent of the prisoners and 73.1 percent of the total commitments in the year 1962.

It was hypothesized earlier that "social policies directed↓ against a particular deviancy affect some deviants differently than others, resulting in a corresponding effect on the larger public." It has previously been suggested that the very nature of public intoxication or drunkenness excludes most middle- and upper-class alcoholics and excessive drinkers who typically drink in private or semi-private surroundings. American socio-cultural values and legal statutes do not condemn individuals for excessive drinking as long as they do not bother

other persons. Thus, public drunkenness laws appear to be aimed at the lower class, and they may be viewed as class laws. There is also evidence which tentatively suggests that, within the lower class, some persons feel the brunt of the law more than others. Both Pittman and Gordon, and later Benz, found that in one northern community Negroes were disproportionately arrested and incarcerated. In 1958, Pittman and Gordon found in their sample of chronic police case inebriates a high proportion of Negroes (18 percent) in comparison to their representation in the general population of the county in which the jail was located (2 percent).[12] In 1962, Benz found that the jail population (both for alcohol and nonalcohol-related offenses) still reflected the differential negative treatment accorded Negroes. The ratio of nonwhite

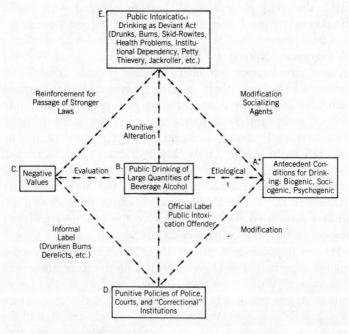

*Letters indicate theoretical sequence of events.
†Arrows indicate theoretical direction of influence.

CHART 2. Model of the Deviancy Reinforcement Cycle for Public Intoxication.

prisoners to nonwhite population in Monroe County for 1962 was 1:16 while the comparable white ratio was 1:273.[11] The jailed intoxication offender represents social problems which encompass both social and class relations in the United States.

Looking at Chart 2, the "Deviancy Reinforcement Cycle for Public Intoxication," we can better see the ramifications of the last statement. Excessive drinking and alcoholism are considered in a moralistic and negative manner by the larger population, no matter what the class position of the deviant or where he does his drinking. (This is true even of professionals who are supposedly more tolerant. For example, the American Medical Association did not officially recognize alcoholism as a disease until 1957.)[13] When their deviant behavior of excessive drinking is acted out in public, "B," the larger community's sanctions become greater, especially since these individuals are much more likely to be found in the lower class and are frequently Negroes; groups typically thought of in a negative manner anyway. Indeed, there seems to be a commonly accepted notion among therapists dealing with problem drinkers and alcoholics that there are two large subtypes. There is the person who has a disease and must be helped (middle- and upper-class alcoholics and problem drinkers), and there is the drunk or Skid-Rowite, who is hopeless and whom few professionals care to treat. Take the case of the chief social worker in a large alcoholism treatment center who, having worked with alcoholics for over ten years, said, "Now and then some pilfering occurred on the Unit, especially if some of the Skid-Row alcoholics were patients." There is also some evidence that public treatment centers seldom treat Skid-Rowites. One of the writers evaluated twenty-two follow-up studies of treated alcoholics. It was found that the typical population in these public treatment facilities excluded lower-lower class whites and, especially, Negroes.[14] This means that the public drunkenness offender cannot expect to find tolerance even among professionals who are reputed to be among the more tolerant groups in the field of alcoholism.

The lower-class public drunkenness offenders are drawn from those who have difficulty in interpersonal relationships, are poorly educated, are frequently from an ethnic or racial minority, and are typically dependent on institutionalized living arrangements (such as those found in the Armed Forces, the Merchant Marine, and the Salvation Army and kindred shelters). In short, they are at a disadvantage in competing with other persons for a productive role in our society.

After repeated arrests and incarcerations, the negative effects of the above sociological variables are reinforced ("D" and "E" on Chart 2). The constantly incarcerated individual finds it nearly impossible to maintain a meaningful marital and familial relationship; his ability to find employment is seriously jeopardized by his arrest record coupled with his poor education. By constantly being officially labeled by the police courts and correctional institutions as a public drunk, he begins to see himself as a public drunk; the jail becomes little more than a shelter to regain his physical strength. Because the public intoxication offender is usually unable to support himself, he frequently turns to petty thievery or jack-rolling. This is especially true if he is an alcoholic. The alcoholic, like the drug addict (many professionals prefer the term alcohol addict), will go to great lengths to maintain his supply of alcohol, and frequently he spends most of his nondrinking hours finding ways (usually illegal) to obtain money for alcohol. As a result, the alcoholic public intoxication offender frequently presents a health problem, not only from diseases associated with an excessive intake of alcohol, but also from his indifference to caring for himself physically.

Social policy has its greatest negative effect on excessive drinkers who are not alcoholics. An excessive drinker who confines his drinking to weekend bouts (a pattern not uncommon in the middle classes), but who does not drink secretively, may find himself frequently arrested or incarcerated. If this happens often enough, he may be socialized by the enforcement of the judicial and correctional processes in such a way as to contribute to his drinking problem. Where before he confined his drinking to weekends and managed to hold a job and be a breadwinner, he now finds these roles increasingly harder to maintain and crises arrive which encourage his drinking. Instead of arresting his excessive drinking, the social policies have modified (relationships between "E"—"A," and "D"—

"A," Chart 2) his deviant behavior and contributed to the development of a more serious deviancy—alcoholism.

Thus, the public intoxication offender confronts the society with a serious social problem which involves the total community as well as the specific institutions of the police, the courts, and correctional institutions. Now the questions should be asked, "Will a change in social policy prevent the deviancy reinforcement cycle?" and, if so, "How does one go about changing social policy?"

One way to alter social policy is to re-educate the general public. By showing the public that public intoxication offenders are not drunks, vagrants, and petty thieves, informal pressure will be exerted on police courts and correctional institutions to change their policy. However, there are two things wrong with this approach. Firstly, public opinion is extremely difficult to re-educate and activate, especially when the subject seldom affects them personally. True, occasionally the newspaper or some civic group will condemn conditions that have allowed some incarcerated public intoxicant to die in his jail cell, but these movements soon pass away. Secondly, and more important, the public may rightfully be apprehensive if it is told that the public intoxicant is not a bum, drunk, and so forth, when in their conceptions they can readily see that he is. In other words, before it can be illustrated that public alcoholics and excessive drinkers are not inherently "evil," the conditions which cause these secondary deviances must be altered. Therefore, the place to intervene in the deviancy reinforcement cycle is at "D," and not "A," the police, courts, and correctional institutions.

Various institutions which execute social policy have a certain degree of autonomy and are able to informally alter social policies. The best way to illustrate how this can be done is to cite examples of how the three institutions (police, courts, and correctional institutions) have, in fact, altered punitive social policies so that they have become therapeutic policies.

Police Intervention

Law enforcement officers in American communities have differential awareness of the magnitude of this problem and varying policies towards the publicly intoxicated person. However, the police are charged by their communities to manage and control the intoxicated person on the street. Almost all communities treat the "drunk on the street" as one who is violating misdemeanor statutes or ordinances which make this behavior a crime. Thus, the publicly intoxicated person is arrested and sent to the municipal court for processing. This is despite the fact that many police officers realize that a holdover or jail is not the appropriate facility for a sick person such as the alcoholic.

In certain cities the police have attempted to intervene in the "revolving door" process, but this is viewed with mixed emotions in America since many feel that the police function is not to rehabilitate offenders; this is best left to other institutions. But when the rehabilitation function is not being performed by other community agencies, the police may attempt intervention. Two notable examples are found in St. Louis and Seattle.

In 1962 and 1963 many key St. Louis police personnel visited the Alcoholism Treatment and Referral Demonstration Project at the Malcolm Bliss Treatment and Research Center and held many information conferences with staff members. As a result of these conferences and further studies, in 1963 the St. Louis Board of Police Commissioners instituted a major policy change in reference to intoxicated persons on the street. The St. Louis Metropolitan Police Department made it mandatory for all individuals "picked up" from the streets of St. Louis to be taken to the emergency rooms of the two city hospitals for physical examination. This means that routine physical evaluation is provided all alcoholics processed by the police; if these individuals are in need of medical care, they are hospitalized instead of being jailed. If medical care is deemed unnecessary, the intoxicated person may be "held until sober"—not more than 20 hours—and released to the community. St. Louis is one of the few American cities in which this innovation in the handling of the public intoxication case has occurred. It squarely places the locus of responsibility for the alcoholic in the treatment sphere and is in keeping with modern practices toward the publicly intoxicated person found in Sweden, Norway, West Germany, Poland, and Czechoslovakia. Hopefully, this breakthrough will be followed by the abandonment of the current primitive and punitive process of jailing public intoxication offenders in the United States.

Another notable example of police intervention was the Seattle Police Department's Rehabilitation Project for Chronic Alcoholics,[15] now currently defunct. Officially opened in August, 1943, it was established by the Police Division which felt that prolonged incarceration of alcoholics did not provide rehabilitation. The chief concern of the project was to allow the alcoholic a chance to reflect about and make changes concerning his drinking problem. The avenue of entry to the project was through the courts. As Jackson, Fagan, and Burr have noted:

> Due to the system of graduated sentences in effect in Seattle, the alcoholic tends to have been arrested five or more times within the year before he becomes eligible for admission to the project. Upon removal to the city jail, the prisoner can ask to be transferred to the rehabilitation project if he sincerely wishes to do something about his drinking problem. All admissions are voluntary. His wish to be transferred is discussed with a police officer who makes a judgement as to whether the man is sincere and would be benefited by this type of project.[15]

Within the project the prisoner became a "patient," and his daily routine was based on a semi-military model. Counseling, lectures, and films concerning alcoholism were provided. A follow-up of men treated within the project indicated that there was a significant reduction in the number of times arrested for public intoxication in the six months following release compared to the six months prior to entry into the project.

Studies in Seattle, Portland, Atlanta, and elsewhere show that intervention by both the police and the courts in the deviancy reinforcement cycle can reduce the number of arrests of the chronic offenders. This occurs without there being any conscious collusion by the police or courts to produce reduced rates for drunkenness. When a program such as that in St. Louis is effected, the police become more understanding of the problem with which they are dealing, and also many other professionals become aware of and begin to treat the alcoholic offender.

Court Intervention

Many municipal judges have become cognizant of the responsibility of the court to public intoxication offenders. Innovations in court processing of inebriates are found in the work of Judge Burnett of Denver and Judge Harrison of Des Moines. Judge Burnett sponsors for court inebriates his Denver Court Honor Class which meets every Monday night; this is basically a "group-therapy" session of alcoholics and problem drinkers organized by the Judge.

Another treatment technique utilized is that of the Half-Way House in Rochester, New York, which was created in response to the Pittman and Gordon study previously cited. A small group of men, instead of being sentenced to the County Jail by the Rochester City judges, are sent to Reception House, a special rehabilitation center in that community. Men for this project are carefully screened for rehabilitation potential by the judges and their staff. Unfortunately, this program covers only a small number of offenders since the rehabilitation staff is unable to absorb more than a few dozen a year. The major purpose of the program is to break the pattern of institutional dependency of court inebriates which has been referred to previously in this paper.

Correctional Institutional Intervention

A critical stage in America's deviancy reinforcement cycle for the chronic drunkenness offender is the workhouse or city jail. Previous research studies have shown that repeated incarceration does not act as a deterrent to the chronic inebriate's behavior. Repeated jailing, as a socially and legally accepted philosophy in the community for reforming the intoxication offender, has been and will continue to be a failure from the rehabilitation point of view. The emphasis in most jails is upon custodial care rather than any systematic treatment regimes for these inebriates. It, however, should be noted that custody does perform certain humanitarian functions. Sentences of a few days to six months for public intoxication fulfills the men's basic needs of shelter and food, and enforces sobriety. Thus, the physical resources of the men are repaired during incarceration, but they can be debilitated at release during another intoxication bender.

Despite the inappropriateness of jails and workhouses, attempts have been made in this context to rehabilitate public intoxication offenders. In 1954, for example, the District of Columbia Workhouse was the setting for a two and one-half year project, utilizing a treatment clinic within the penal institution. Both individual and group therapies were used, but the prisoners participating had been screened; therefore, the improvement rate—one-third of those participating—was higher than would be expected for an unselected sample.

True, these few examples of policy changes have not affected the overall problem of the public drunkenness offender, but these attempts do show that intervention is possible; this is not to say that intervention is easy. Current institutions which handle the problem (jails, workhouses, and municipal courts) *may* have a vested interest in the maintenance of the *status quo*. In some communities the emphasis is on the economic contributions of the offenders through their work on local roads and civic projects. There are American municipalities which actually budget the expected services of the offenders to their local civic projects.

The best examples of the positive effect social policies can have on the public drunkenness offender are found outside the United States. In the Scandinavian countries, it is indicated that enforced treatment for alcoholism and excessive drinking can be beneficial. If we view the alcoholic individual as being not only one who is suffering from a chronic disease, but, in the case of the chronic intoxication offender, one whose behavior is a nuisance to society, then we can construct a case for compulsory intervention by public health measures. Experience has shown that enforced custodial care at a penal institution has not positively altered the behavior of the public intoxicant; if anything, it reinforces the deviancy. Therefore, we should perhaps attempt to create compulsory treatment facilities, much in the same sense as they have been established for tubercular cases, and compulsory out-patient treatment facilities such as those which exist for venereal disease. Thus, the deviancy reinforcement cycle for the public intoxication offender might be broken.

9

The Legal Control of Alcoholism: Towards a Public Health Concept

PETER BARTON HUTT

Under early English common law, public intoxication was not, in itself, a crime. Only drunkenness accompanied by a public nuisance or a breach of the peace was considered criminal.[1]

Mere public intoxication was first made a criminal offense by an English statute in 1606:[2]

AN ACT FOR REPRESSING THE ODIOUS AND LOATHSOME
SIN OF DRUNKENNESS

WHEREAS, the loathsome and odious sin of drunkenness is of late grown into common use within this realm, being the root and foundation of many other enormous sins, as bloodshed, stabbing, murder, swearing, fornication, adultery, and such like, the great dishonor of God, and of our nation, the overthrow of many good arts and manual trades, the disabling of divers workmen, and the general impoverishing of many good subjects, abusively wasting the good creatures of God:

THOSE not familiar with legal citations may locate the materials referred to in the references by consulting any law librarian.

II.   Be it therefore enacted . . . That all and every person or persons, which shall be drunk, . . . shall for every such offense forfeit and lose five shillings, . . . to be paid . . . to the hands of the churchwardens . . . ;[12] and if the offender or offenders be not able to pay . . . shall be committed to the stocks for every offense, there to remain by the space of six hours.

And public intoxication remains a criminal offense, with varying penalties, in England and virtually every part of the United States today.

The initial legal recognition of what is now known as chronic alcoholism appeared in Lord Hale's classic treatise, *Pleas of the Crown*, written in about 1675 but not published until 1736.[12] Lord Hale, who is credited with being the first legal authority to undertake any significant analysis of the relationship of mental disease and the criminal law, concluded that drunkenness would not excuse criminal activity except (1) when it was caused by the "stratagem or fraud of another," or (2) when long-continued drinking had resulted in an "habitual and fixed phrenzy"—which appears to be an early description of alcoholism. In time, the courts recognized Lord Hale's first exception as an example of the broader common law rule that *involuntary behavior* cannot be criminal, and his second exception as an example of the broader rule that *insanity* excuses what would otherwise be criminal conduct. An awareness of the fundamental tension between the "involuntary behavior" and the "insanity" rules is essential to an understanding of the handling of alcoholics in our courts during the past one hundred years.

The "involuntary behavior" rule applies broadly to all human behavior. Its rationale is that it would be inhuman, as well as futile, to punish an individual for behavior which he lacked the capacity to control.

The term "insanity," on the other hand, describes just one of many possible causes of involuntary behavior. Judicial use of this term would have caused no problem if its content were analyzed and applied in terms of the more basic standard of voluntariness. Regrettably, however, the judiciary rapidly moved on to a new standard. The famous *M'Naghten's Case*, in 1843, enunciated what is now the prevailing rule, that the defense of insanity is applicable only when the defendant did not know the difference between right and wrong.[5]

The conflict between the basic "involuntary behavior" rule and the narrower definition of "insanity" in *M'Naghten's Case* soon became apparent. A New York court, grappling with this conflict in the specific context of alcoholism, noted that although the alcoholic drinks involuntarily he does know the difference between right and wrong.[6] Unfortunately, that court, and hundreds of others that followed it, chose to adhere to the more widely-accepted rule of *M'Naghten's Case*.

In order to reconcile the inconsistent application of these two principles, the courts resorted to a legal fiction. All drinking by a chronic alcoholic was deemed, as a matter of law, to be "voluntary," on the theory that even the alcoholic had initially been a voluntary drinker before becoming an alcoholic and therefore should be held accountable for his subsequent disease.[7] Under this legal fiction, a chronic alcoholic was held criminally responsible for his public intoxication, as well as for any other antisocial conduct caused by his drinking, even though that intoxication and resulting conduct were the unavoidable products of his alcoholism.

In only one unique decision was this general rule rejected. In the case of *State* v. *Pike*, decided in 1869, the defendant was charged with murder.[3] The New Hampshire Supreme Court held that the questions whether alcoholism is a disease, whether the defendant was suffering from alcoholism, and whether the murder was the product of the defendant's alcoholism, were all questions of fact relevant to determining the defendant's criminal responsibility. In a remarkable concurring opinion Judge Doe, one of this country's early great jurists, admonished the legal profession not to permit ancient medical beliefs, long since discredited, to become encrusted as legal principles:

Defective medical theories [have] usurped the position of common-law principles.

The usurpation, when detected, should cease. The manifest imposture of an extinct medical theory pretending to be legal authority, cannot appeal for support to our reason or even to our sympathy. The proverbial reverence for precedent, does not readily yield; but when it comes to be understood that a precedent is medicine and not law, the reverence in which it is held, will, in the course of time, subside (Note 3 at 438).

Judge Doe recognized that "When disease is the propelling, uncontrollable power, the man is as innocent as the weapon," and thus that, if alcoholism had driven an individual involuntarily to commit murder, he could not be convicted for even so serious an involuntary act. But the *Pike* decision stood alone for almost a century.

It is difficult to explain the judicial adherence for such a long period of time to the legal fiction that, because alcoholism is a voluntarily-acquired disease, an alcoholic's drinking must also be deemed to be "voluntary." It has long been the rule, for example, that voluntarily induced insanity still excuses what would otherwise be criminal conduct. Indeed, where long-continued voluntary drinking leads to insanity (rather than merely alcoholism), the courts have always acknowledged that antisocial conduct caused by that insanity cannot be criminal.[8] One is left, then, with the observation that the history of judicial precedents in the field of alcoholism is explainable primarily as reflecting moralistic principles, and a consequent reluctance to accept modern medical knowledge.[9] As one commentator has suggested, in attempting to explain the more rapid judicial acceptance of medical advances in the field of mental illness, "traditional attitudes of hostility towards drunkenness render rational and just determination more difficult than in insanity cases."[4]

The decisions in *Easter* v. *District of Columbia*[10] and *Driver* v. *Hinnant*,[11] which were handed down by two Federal Courts of Appeals in early 1966, reflect none of this traditional hostility. They have, instead, applied modern knowledge about alcoholism to determine the criminal responsibility of chronic alcoholics. In *Easter*, the U. S. Court of Appeals for the District of Columbia Circuit held that the well-settled common-law principle—that conduct cannot be criminal unless it is *voluntary*—precludes the conviction of an alcoholic for public intoxication. In *Driver*, the U. S. Court of Appeals for the Fourth Circuit held that to convict a chronic alcoholic for public intoxication, and thus to ignore the common-law principle followed in *Easter*, violates the prohibition against cruel and unusual punishment contained in the Eighth Amendment to the United States Constitution.

These cases constitute a unique and desirable merger of common-law doctrine and Constitutional command. They squarely reject the long-standing legal fiction that all drinking by a chronic alcoholic is voluntary as a matter of law. Instead, they accept, as established facts, that chronic alcoholism is a disease and that the chronic alcoholic drinks involuntarily.

The full ramifications of the *Easter* and *Driver* decisions are not yet known, of course, and can scarcely be predicted. It would appear, however, that the judicial principles they enunciate have wide-ranging implications for the entire field of alcoholism. At a minimum, they *require* that the problem of the chronic alcoholic court offender be taken out of the courts. If properly utilized by workers in the field, moreover, they may produce a broad and determined commitment by the public as a whole to the treatment of alcoholism as a disease and the rehabilitation of alcoholics as useful citizens. Certainly, these decisions point the way towards public rejection of the moralistic criminal view of alcoholism and its recognition as a public health problem of major proportions.

PART IV

The Treatment of
Alcoholics:
Some Social
Considerations

10

The Open Door:
Sociology in an Alcoholism
Treatment Facility

DAVID J. PITTMAN

BACKGROUND

This chapter is concerned with the role that I played as a sociologist in the development, planning, and operation of a special treatment facility for alcoholics in a university-affiliated, municipal psychiatric hospital in St. Louis, Missouri. Furthermore, this account is a study in social change explicitly focusing upon planned intervention in the community's care for alcoholics.

The story begins in the fall of 1958, when I added to my Department of Sociology role a three-fourths time appointment as a sociologist with the Department of Psychiatry at Washington University. My appointment to the Medical School faculty was the first such appointment of a sociologist, although several sociologists were supported within the Department by research projects with outside financial support. My instructions at the time from the Chairman of Psychiatry were quite open-ended, namely, develop a research program in a significant social psychiatric area. My decision to focus

REPRINTED with permission of The Dorsey Press, David J. Pittman, "The Open Door: Sociology in an Alcoholism Treatment Facility," in Arthur B. Shostak (ed.), *Sociology in Action*, 1966.

Supported (in part) by a Mental Health Project Grant (MH657) from the National Institute of Mental Health, U.S. Public Health Service.

on alcoholism stemmed in large part from my 10 years of research in Rochester, New York, concerning the chronic drunkenness offender[1, 2] and the fact that I had recently signed a contract to co-edit a book in the area of drinking patterns.[3]

THE ALCOHOLIC AT BLISS IN 1958

For some years the University-affiliated Malcolm Bliss Hospital, an acute admitting and short-term psychiatric treatment institution, had accepted approximately 800 alcoholics yearly. Specializing in the care of seriously disturbed mentally ill persons, the hospital had neither a regular alcoholism treatment unit nor any special treatment program for the alcoholic; therefore, for the most part only a 24–48 hour drying-out service was offered. Alcoholics could not stay longer unless another psychiatric diagnosis was appended.

In this situation, I came to believe, with the concurrence of the Hospital Director, that Bliss needed a special in-patient treatment facility on a separate ward for alcoholic patients. Our impression was that the general hospitals in the community were unsympathetic to the dilemma of the alcoholic.[4−6] Furthermore, significant numbers of hospitals refused to admit patients with a primary diagnosis of alcoholism, and others (including Bliss) required the alcoholic to be hospitalized in the psychiatric unit. No other hospital in the area except Bliss showed an interest in the creation of a treatment program for the indigent alcoholic. Our plan was to develop a special treatment facility for alcoholics with social and medical therapies geared to their particular problems.

GRASS ROOTS AND PUBLIC RELATIONS

Neither the St. Louis City Hospital Division, of which Bliss was a part, nor Washington University had available funds to create a special treatment facility (a situation possibly related to a low priority assigned the treatment needs of alcoholics). We, however, did have an unused hydrotherapy ward on the Bliss Ground South floor which could be converted to an alcoholism unit. As this ward, however, was located directly above the steam pipe lines, it would be usable only if air conditioned. This added considerably to the projected costs and created strains immediately with the rest of the hospital staff who were in nonair-conditioned space.[7]

The obtaining of funds to create a public facility for alcoholics loomed from the start as a formidable obstacle. Previously, in 1955, a local St. Louis group composed of physicians and other citizens had attempted to raise money to begin a local council on alcoholism. Their efforts brought forth only $400 in contributions, and their movement collapsed. After this abortive effort a local public relations executive advised the group to wait until there was an event of consequence that "would trigger interest in the plight of the alcoholic in St. Louis."

In the fall of 1958, the event occurred. An alcoholic veteran of World War II, who had been previously hospitalized in Bliss, committed suicide while his wife was on the telephone attempting to secure help for him. This alcoholic refused to return to a facility where he would be hospitalized among mental patients.[8] A local reporter, Marguerite Shepard, of the *Globe-Democrat,* by her stories about this tragic occurrence, the military funeral for him, and subsequent articles,[9] brought into community awareness the lack of adequate public treatment facilities.

Thus, in late 1958, the ingredients for a community attempt to create a public facility were present in three forms—namely, (1) the tragic event of an alcoholic's suicide; (2) intensive coverage of the alcoholism problem by the mass media; (3) leadership in the presence of Dr. George A. Ulett, Bliss Director, myself and others. Our immediate goal was to create "an alcoholism center" by converting unused space at Bliss into a 30-bed treatment facility. The first projected cost was $64,000 for the remodeling. The cost for additional treatment personnel had been promised by the City of St. Louis.

Dr. Ulett, the Bliss Director, and I attended scores of
meetings with ministers, Alcoholics Anonymous members,
physicians, and church auxiliaries, and appeared on numerous radio and television shows to explain our treatment center
and the necessity for public support. We also recruited a
number of citizens who volunteered to solicit industry for
funds. To help in this drive, we prepared a small brochure
entitled, "Alcoholism Center for the St. Louis Community—
Here's Why We Need It and Here's How We Can Get It."

In due course, the community's characteristic lethargy was
broken.[10, 11] A pledge of $5,000 was obtained in February,
1958, from the McDonnell Aircraft Corporation, the largest
employer in the state, and in one sense our effort became
respectable—and successful. In May, 1959, our drive assumed
an organized form through the appointment by Mayor Raymond Tucker of an effective Citizen's Committee to raise
funds for the treatment center.[12]

This particular experience focused my awareness upon the
fact that social innovations in society's handling, processing,
and care for particular problem groups rarely come from the
traditional institutional structures, whether they be private
agencies or state governmental departments. For example, the
mental health movement is especially indebted to the mental
patients, Dorothea Dix and Clifford Beers; changing concepts
of the alcoholic as being a legitimate group for social concern
largely date back to the pioneers in Alcoholics Anonymous;
and currently, innovations in the care of the narcotics addict
are being spearheaded by Synanon. As a sociologist I was
aware that our effort would face resistance from traditional
care-taking agencies; I was more surprised to discover desire
for change in the care of alcoholics was deeply rooted in
significant community power groups. More specifically, while
Alcoholics Anonymous *per se* is not a powerful organization
in any community, some of its individual members do occupy
positions of high prestige and power. This fact worked to
our advantage in that several "recovered" alcoholics joined
our effort and were able to help secure the cooperation of
the business and political elite in the community.

In summary, our success was directly related to our having

mobilized at the grass roots level a climate which was favorable to change, but, more important, elements of the power structure of the community supported our goals.

PLANNING THE TREATMENT FACILITY

After the appointment of the Mayor's fund-raising Citizens' Committee in May, 1959, I was confident that an alcoholism facility would be obtained. Therefore, in conjunction with Dr. Ulett, I began planning the program for the facility. Our planning divided into two parts: (1) community, and (2) hospital aspects.

COMMUNITY PLANNING

I felt our hospital unit would operate more effectively if we possessed systematic knowledge about existing community attitudes and resources in the area of alcoholism. To this end, funds were secured from the Missouri Division of Health to complete a sociological survey[13] of the extent and location of the alcoholism problem in Metropolitan St. Louis, the existing community services and resources for handling the problem, and the attitudes of community agency personnel toward alcoholism as a disease, its treatability, and the alcoholic patient or client's role performance. Such sociological information promised to give us not only an indication of scope and attitudes, but also a base line against which to measure changes in the community after an alcoholism program was instituted. (Briefly stated,[14-16] the survey uncovered a substantial alcoholism problem in the metropolitan area, with approximately 56,000 persons, or 6 per cent of the population 20 years of age and over, estimated to be alcoholic. This was coupled with the finding of disinclination by hospitals and agencies to render services in the area of alcoholism.)

It was from this on-going study of the community that the decision was made to gear the new Alcoholism Treatment and Research Center (A.T.R.C.) toward a demonstration mental health project model eligible for support by the United States

Public Health Service.[17] Thus, the community study focussed our attention on planning a facility that would emphasize in-patient treatment and systematic referral of alcoholics to appropriate community agencies.

PLANNING THE HOSPITAL UNIT

In constructing and planning the A.T.R.C. an attempt was made to incorporate basic sociological principles concerning group and organizational structures into the physical design and treatment program.

Briefly stated, the A.T.R.C. is a 30-bed unit within a 228-bed acute psychiatric hospital. It is a separate ward and contains only those patients whose primary diagnosis at admission is alcoholism. (The rationale for a separate facility has been presented earlier.) The unit has its own dining room, lounging area, snack bar, reading room, and group therapy room (known as the community room). Auxiliary resources of occupational therapy, recreational therapy, and volunteer programs centering in other sections of the hospital are also available to the patients.

The offices of the professional personnel, i.e., social workers, physicians, and nurses, are located within the unit. This reduces the social and physical distance between the staff and patients, allows intensive observation of patient behavior and creates a favorable physical climate for the development of a community of alcoholics and non-alcoholics. As we believed there was no reason for isolating the acute cases of alcoholism for treatment (cases involving delirium tremens, alcoholic hallucinosis, and related complications) we made provision for two single rooms (referred to as acute treatment rooms) on the unit. Our assumption was that acute cases would respond to treatment better if they were surrounded by ambulatory patients and received intensive nursing care. Thus, the community of patients could help those patients sicker than they.[18] Finally, across from the group therapy room is the nurses' station, with sliding glass windows which allow easy observation of both sections of the unit.

This air-conditioned and attractively decorated facility, composed of beds for 24 men, four women, and two single-acute treatment rooms, is furnished in a homey, comfortable fashion. Our major effort was to remove the ward as far as possible from the "drunk tank," so typical of American municipal hospitals.

FRICTION AT THE "BLISS-HILTON"

Since the fund drive had been successful, the nursing staff was designated by Dr. Ulett to choose the beds, bedside tables, chairs, lamps, and so forth, for the facility. Mostly selected were modernistic hospital furnishings, which stood in bold relief to the shabby institutional furniture in the rest of the hospital. The new equipment, coupled with air-conditioned facilities, led that part of the hospital not connected with the A.T.R.C. to refer to it as the "Bliss-Hilton" even before it received patients.

Hostility to both alcoholics and the unit took many different forms. One "organically oriented" psychiatrist on observing the glass windows on the nursing station stated: "They [the glass windows] will only last a week. Some drunk will break them." One laboratory technician when viewing the three-foot lamps unsecured on two tables in the T.V. room remarked, "You'd better bolt them down before the patients are admitted." At this time most of the friction remained under control because of the charismatic leadership exercised by Dr. Ulett.

OPEN DOORS

The treatment context was outlined in great detail in the demonstration application before the facility opened. As a sociologist I strongly influenced our choice of the treatment model of a therapeutic community with its emphasis upon group living, group psychotherapy, and patient responsibility.[19] An account of the A.T.R.C. during its early months when I served as Program Director follows:

The Alcoholism Centre, run on an open-ward basis, is modelled along the lines of a therapeutic community. Thus, the staff functions on a team basis, interacts frequently and permissively with the patients encouraging, but not requiring them to participate fully in the programme, and discusses the alcoholic's programme with him or her according to the patient's desires.

Furthermore, the staff emphasises the creation of patient groups for therapeutic purposes. An unstructured group therapy session is led three times a week by the psychiatrist, internist, or social worker. Furthermore, there are four small intensive therapy groups conducted by social workers and psychiatrists. On the three alternate week days, structured therapeutic sessions are held for the imparting of information materials on alcoholism and personality development. Group meetings are held three evenings a week, two of them conducted by Alcoholics Anonymous personnel, and the third, a group therapy session which patients and their families may attend. All patients are urged to return to the Centre for weekly group therapy sessions, held in conjunction with the current group of in-patients.

The staff has encouraged the development of a patient self-government system which mobilises patient responsibility for helping more acutely ill patients and for light housekeeping tasks. The purpose of this system is to engender patient responsibility for their behaviour which we hope will continue after discharge. To encourage self-government, an opportunity has been provided for weekly patient meetings from which the staff are excluded.

These in- and out-patient groups are organised not only for their inherent therapeutic properties but for the establishment of non-drinking groups in the hospital which will extend beyond the patient's stay and act as a partial deterrent to community drinking groups.[20]

ORGANIZATIONAL PROBLEMS

The history of the A.T.R.C. has been marked by four problems in social organization relevant to the sociologist who would work in a medical setting.

For one, shortly before our unit opened the Superintendent and Medical Director (Dr. Ulett) resigned to become Director of the Division of Mental Diseases of Missouri. Unlike her predecessor the new hospital director had minimal identification with the alcoholism unit. Succession in leadership often brings about increasing bureaucratization; this proved the case at Bliss.[21] Staff members of A.T.R.C. were expected to rigidly adhere to all rules and regulations in the *Hospital Manual of Procedure,* to "clear" all communications with the outside through the Director's office, and to have all policy decisions involving the unit approved by the Bliss Hospital Policy Committee.

Second, a major cleavage associated with bureaucratization developed around the treatment ideology which guided the A.T.R.C., for our philosophy contrasted with that employed in other sections of the hospital. Our unit was developed and operated as an open-door facility, emphasizing the therapeutic community approach and employing the mental health treatment team concept. This was a radical departure in treatment ideology for Bliss personnel who reflected an organic and psychopharmacological approach—one which I term "organic pessimism" in contrast to the "environmental optimism" of the therapeutic community.

The treatment schism was symbolized in locked and open doors. All wards in Bliss prior to the opening of the A.T.R.C. were locked,[22] and there was much concern about allowing our unit to be unlocked. When the Hospital Policy Committee approved the unlocked doors, one psychiatrist stated: "Why don't we try it locked for a couple of months and see how it works." The anxiety around unlocked doors was so great that on the first night after opening, one psychiatric resident who was having difficulty with an agitated patient locked the door for a couple of hours. The next day the resident was reprimanded, and this never occurred again. The "Open-Door" became a symbol around which we in the A.T.R.C. integrated ourselves. We explained to patients in their group meetings that this procedure was being evaluated, and it was up to them whether the door would stay open. In the first six months no patients from the A.T.R.C. "eloped" (left without permission), although several patients "eloped" from the locked wards. Furthermore, the patients named their ward newspaper *The Open Door.*

A third problem reflected basic dilemmas in the role definitions assigned to treatment personnel. The more *traditional* definitions of treatment in medicine and psychiatry see it as being exercised by the well-trained physician involving basically medical techniques and utilizing in a subordinate status position nurses, attendants, social workers, and psychologists. Milieu therapy defines treatment in the broadest context of the total environment of the patient. Thus, the physical facility, the personnel, whether the charwoman or the psychiatrist, the patients themselves, and the patients' relatives are all ingredients in the treatment process. Furthermore, the principles of environmental therapy place great emphasis upon an equalitarian ethos in the treatment team. This approach by its very nature is threatening to some hospital personnel, particularly those with an upward mobility syndrome.

Finally, a problem in social organization relevant to the sociologist turns on the fact that his role in a treatment context is a problematic one at best. Since this hospital had no previous sociologists and since I succeeded in being differentiated early in the planning from the social workers and the psychologists, it was difficult for the medical personnel to assign me a position in the status hierarchy. It was known that I performed research; this was positively evaluated as this hospital was connected with a university medical center. But my sociological role in relation to the organization of treatment services in the A.T.R.C. was never really accepted. Occasionally, psychiatric residents would report to me the concern of certain psychiatric supervisors that "Dr. ———— says that you're going to run the alcoholism unit when it opens." It must be stated that at no time was it expected that I would assume charge of the total A.T.R.C. operation; I, however, was to be the chief of the demonstration project grant.[23] These incidents, however, highlight the concern that some medical personnel expressed about their prerogatives in reference to the treatment function.[24]

CONCLUSIONS: HOSPITAL AND COMMUNITY INNOVATIONS

The question of whether our planned intervention in the community's care of the alcoholic succeeded in a strictly scientific sense is still being measured. In our minds, however, there is no question of our success in instituting basic sociological principles in the treatment process of this hospital. The 30-bed therapeutic community for alcoholics at Bliss still operates on this model with the doors open; for all practical purposes the program remains as originally created.

The greatest success of our intervention has come in the area of changing the treatment methods and attitudes of community agencies and hospitals that deal with the alcoholic. Only one example will be mentioned: In late 1963, key police personnel visited the A.T.R.C. and held many informal conferences with our staff members. In early 1964, the St. Louis Metropolitan Police Department made it mandatory for all individuals "picked up" from the streets of St. Louis to be taken to the emergency rooms of the two city hospitals for physical examination. This means that routine physical evaluation is provided all alcoholics processed by the police; if these individuals are in need of medical care, they are hospitalized instead of being jailed. This is one of the few American cities in which this innovation in the handling of the public intoxication case has occurred. Hopefully, this breakthrough will be followed by the abandonment of the current primitive process of jailing public problem drinkers; if so, it will be in no small measure the consequence of the efforts of applied sociologists.

11

Social Therapies
in the Treatment of Alcoholics

LAURA ESTHER ROOT

INTRODUCTION

In the past, alcoholics have been neglected, punished, committed to mental institutions, and a few have been treated in private sanitariums. Many have died as a result of their drinking, either in the acute phase or due to the additional physical illnesses resulting from alcoholism. For many years alcoholics who could afford it were sent to private hospitals "to take the cure" (a process of clearing the alcohol out of the body—"drying out"), and, when released, ultimately returned to drinking. Other types of alcoholics, such as revolving door alcoholics,[1] have spent most of their lives in jails, yet incarceration does nothing to cure a drinking problem. For those committed to mental institutions, some stayed years or for shorter periods of time, with the usual result, a return to drinking following discharge.

PIONEER ALCOHOLISM GROUP THERAPY

The most successful approach is used by Alcoholics Anonymous (A.A.) who first initiated alcoholism group therapy as a means of maintaining sobriety. Since the 1930s, A.A. has utilized the group meeting approach, which is an effective tool in maintaining sobriety for thousands of Americans annu-

SUPPORTED (in part) by a Mental Health Project Grant (MH657) from the National Institute of Mental Health, United States Public Health Service.

ally. Some of their success appears to be based upon the opportunity of the individual to share his problem with others who have a like problem in a large group meeting held regularly. Al-Anon and Ala-Teen for the nondrinking members of the alcoholic's family are proving very effective organizations, utilizing some of the same techniques as A.A.

THERAPIES IN TREATMENT

For the past decade or so, professional people working with alcoholics have found some techniques for treatment which have proved effective in helping the alcoholic with his problem. Research demonstration projects, pilot studies, experimental treatments (including new drugs), and new types of settings have been explored to find the most effective tools and methods in working with alcoholics. Some of these therapies have been tried individually, while others have been applied as collective techniques with the alcoholic. In this chapter, the various types of therapies which have proved effective, when used in a multifaceted approach to treatment, will be described and discussed.

If social therapies are combined, with a good physical and medical treatment regimen in an ideal setting, they provide the optimum in treatment for patients with a drinking problem. This treatment is not designed exclusively for the chronic addictive drinkers; it can include other types of alcoholics such as those whom Jellinek[2] has described in *The Disease Concept of Alcoholism*. The neurotic alcoholics, and the problem drinkers who are not yet addicted to alcohol can also be treated with this regimen. Some of these therapies have been used previously by various disciplines in treatment for other disorders; however, they have either been modified or adapted to the treatment of the alcoholic. These techniques include the therapeutic community, as originally designed and employed by Maxwell Jones,[3] the multidisciplinary team, the location of team members' offices on the unit or ward (borrowed from medical teaching hospitals), the use of group therapy, and didactic lectures and films.

PHYSICAL SETTING

Treatment for the alcoholic should be provided in an environment which is conducive to it, rather than in a locked facility including bars on the windows. The physical setting for the in-patient care of alcoholics then sets the stage for further treatment. It is preferable to have an in-patient treatment facility located in a building of its own. If this is not possible, however, it should be situated on a ground floor with a separate outside entrance, with an appropriate name for the facility, in a general hospital setting. This is to relieve the alcoholics from being threatened by their admission, as compared to going to jail or mental institutions. Many alcoholics are unable to seek admission on their own, but need assistance in obtaining treatment and care.

The facility must be light and airy, with enough floor space to provide care for alcoholics in various stages of the disorder without the usual hospital atmosphere. The physical design is arranged so that it will provide rooms for both male and female patients, as well as rooms for patients who must have special care during withdrawal stages. Furniture, including beds for patients, should be selected to provide necessary needs for the acutely ill patients, yet not have an institutional look. In one facility, an attractive walnut wood was selected for hospital bedroom furniture instead of white metal customarily used in a hospital setting. One of the myths which remains concerning treatment of the alcoholics, is the need for severe restraints and furniture which will withstand their violent behavior. This was never the truth. Patients in the acute stages of alcoholism will cause no more disturbance than those with any other acute disease, whether medical, surgical, or psychiatric, if they are properly medicated and treated.

The lounges and group therapy rooms, as well as all staff offices, should be furnished to create a warm, comfortable, and accepting atmosphere. Staff offices for the members of the team should be located on the unit and be large enough so that small group sessions can be held in them when necessary. The importance in the physical setting of the location of staff offices is to provide availability of the staff to patients and to encourage permissive interaction between them.

The desirability of a separate entrance to the unit serves as a symbol of trust to the alcoholic patients when the door is left open. One of the early methods of treating alcoholics, which unfortunately still remains in some facilities, was to lock the door. This approach, of course, identifies with the moralistic rejection which society has placed upon alcoholism.

If the physical setting is designed as described above, it provides the basis for the first social therapy which will be discussed; the treatment environment or the therapeutic "milieu" which is created within the unit. The purpose of this therapeutic community, which has been modified for the treatment of alcoholics, is to establish an environmental milieu within which, structurally, the facility encourages the inter-action and participation by patients at all levels of treatment in a communal way. Another factor in their collective unit is the ward government, which is a vital part of the modified therapeutic community. Patients assume responsible roles in keeping the unit clean and neat and in settling disagreements which may arise. Together with the staff, the patients make necessary suggestions and plans for each other, not only during their in-patient stay, but also assist each other in discharge planning and recommended aftercare plans. One of the greatest supports for in-patients is to see a former patient return to the unit for a group therapy session, didactic lecture, or an A.A. group, looking well and holding down a job. He is a visual example of what the in-patients can ac-complish when they are discharged. In an atmosphere of understanding and acceptance by a trained, skilled staff, the alcoholics begin to understand that they are sick people who can be helped with their disease, and they can return to a new way of life without alcohol. Understanding, acceptance, tolerance, patience, and availability are the key tools used by the staff in the modified therapeutic community for the care of alcoholics. This type of treatment for alcoholics has been used successfully in England, The Netherlands, and in the United States.

THE PROFESSIONAL TEAM

The multidisciplinary team, an important part of the therapeutic community, is generally composed of a psychiatrist,
psychologist, nurse, and social worker. For alcoholics, a multidisciplinary team, having an internist, sociologist, vocational
counselor, psychologist, resident psychiatrist, nurse, social
worker, and lay counselors, is the most effective group in providing treatment. Team members must accept and respect
each other for their knowledge, skills, and experience. Above
all, they must have a knowledge of alcoholism and an attitude
of acceptance of alcoholics as sick human beings. In working
in the modified therapeutic milieu, roles of each of the team
members must coincide with the social organization in the
ward. The importance of individual professional status is
minimized, while the team and its interaction with patients
is emphasized. In the past, the roles of the physician, psychologist, and social worker have been stressed, whereas in the
modified therapeutic community for alcoholics, the roles of
nurses, counseling aids, attendants, licensed practical nurses,
maintenance personnel, and diet maids have assumed a right-
ful importance within the community. In treating alcoholics,
the individual staff member to whom the patient relates most
readily should be assigned to work with him.

In one facility, a cleaning lady was the one staff person
with whom a particular alcoholic patient could establish rap-
port. She, with the aid of other team members, worked very
successfully to help this alcoholic. Another patient sought out
a licensed practical nurse on night duty, who counseled him.
She, in turn, was given guidance and direction by the team
in morning meetings before she went off duty. The important
factor to be considered in the treatment milieu, is the progress
of the alcoholics and not the individual discipline's status as to
whom should treat patients. In the modified therapeutic community, then, it is the team effort which is the most important.
As the various disciplines begin to learn to work together
and respect each other's experience and knowledge, they bene-

fit all the patients in the milieu. These combinations of the skills aid alcoholic patients, not only in the acute stage, but also during their stay in the facility, as well as for essential aftercare.

It may seem incongruous to consider the physical setting, the therapeutic milieu, and the multidisciplinary team as part of social therapy, but this is a necessary fact. Unless these three components are present and functioning well, the specific treatments which include group therapy, sociodrama, individual counseling, didactic lectures, and films cannot be the effective tools they should be. Therefore, assuming that a facility is well designed, staffed with a multidisciplinary team in a modified therapeutic community, the treatment of alcoholics begins the moment they come through the door of the unit. The atmosphere is one of acceptance, understanding, and willingness to treat these individuals for their disease, and it is the rare alcoholic who does not respond to this environment. If the patients are in the withdrawal stage, they must be treated for this (sometimes referred to as "drying out" or detoxification). A specific treatment regimen is prescribed by the physician, and most patients will respond and are ambulatory in one to two days. After the patients are detoxified, they are usually assigned to one of the bedrooms and further treatment begins.

ALCOHOLISM AND GROUP THERAPY

Group therapy is one of the most important techniques in the treatment of the alcoholic. Group therapy is the treatment of choice for most alcoholics because of its effectiveness. Group therapy, used in the treatment of alcoholics, is different than group psychotherapy used with many psychiatrically ill and/or emotionally disturbed patients. Group therapy for alcoholism is more reality based in everyday living situations and in the problems involved in maintaining sobriety. The groups are large, with as many as thirty or more patients in them. The groups are heterogeneous, in that they combine patients as to age, sex, race, religion, and marital status—no one is restricted from the group. The groups are homogeneous in that all patients share a common problem—alcoholism.

The importance of having a heterogeneous group provides the individual patient with an opportunity to see others who are suffering from the same disease. Thus a housewife might be sitting next to a teacher, a truckdriver, an indigent alcoholic, a lawyer, a social worker, a nurse, or a minister. The individual patient begins to realize that here are people from different strata of society or a similar stratum, who are going, or have gone through, similar experiences with their drinking problem. An awareness that their individual experience with the inability to control alcohol ingestion and its resultant problems is not unique to them occurs within the group sessions.

It is important to consider the setting or location where group therapy sessions are held. It is important to have a well-lighted room with, if possible, a small raised platform across one end which could be, when necessary, used as a stage for sociodrama or for lecturing. It is well to have a portable blackboard or a wall blackboard at the back of the platform (which may be used for didactic lectures and illustrations during a group session). Comfortable arm chairs are arranged in a semicircle, so that the therapist is able to see all patients and observe all responses, movements, as well as the shades of expressions on their faces. They also must be within the therapist's peripheral vision during the session, since much may be learned from nonverbal gestures as well as from the discussion.

What occurs then in the alcoholism group therapy sessions? Discussions are often spontaneous and unstructured, yet sometimes patterns emerge and follow a design around a particular topic. If group spontaneity is slow, the therapist can initiate or increase it by using a patient as a leader of the group, by a specific topic, and/or by using two or three patients to act as discussants for that session.

Every alcoholic has his own reason for drinking, and sometimes in the open discussions in the group many of the difficult problems which he has encountered concerning this are brought into the open. This, in turn, sometimes brings a wider discussion, which aids him in gaining some insight into his drinking problem. The majority of alcoholics tend to feel trapped in their disease. They feel that they are helpless and are ruled by "the bottle." Once alcoholics become addicted, they continue to seek and maintain their "never-never land" where all their troubles disappear. They can, in "this state," be impervious to the fact that they may be losing their job, or have lost it, as well as their family, friends, and position in society. In this state then they remain free for a while from all of their troubles—they are able to forget.

There is a self-destructive element in alcoholism, which many patients are unable to see. However, within the group therapy sessions, through an exchange of ideas, alcoholics are often able to create a foundation from which they are eventually able to make a "self-inventory" as it is termed in A.A. This is a careful evaluation of one's individual self, emphasizing strengths and weaknesses. If this is attempted too soon with most alcoholics, they will feel threatened; in fact, they may disappear from the group. In the large group, however, they are least threatened, and consequently they are able to come to this task more readily with the support and encouragement of their fellow patients and the therapist.

It is important for alcoholism group therapy that the groups be both educational and didactic as well as therapeutic. This does not mean that the therapist becomes a visiting teacher, or host, but rather that the knowledge of the disease is incorporated into group discussions. Another important factor in this type of therapy is group participation. The group interacts more readily if there is permissiveness and understanding on the part of both the therapists and the patients. The nonjudgmental atmosphere created in therapy sessions helps the alcoholic to begin his "self-inventory," or "self-scrutiny," which is a necessary step in his recovery. Furthermore, the group climate helps him to view his behavior in terms of the defenses surrounding his drinking problem and his everyday life situations. He is able to gain some perspective, usually for the first time.

Most alcoholics go through phases in their addiction to alcohol, and in an early phase many tend to rationalize why they drink. Some say it is because of their wife's nagging, or perhaps they have encountered difficulty on the job, or trouble with the employer, and so forth. They also will admit they drink to ease the tensions and the annoyances of everyday life. Then there is a phase during which the alcoholic usually projects and blames a new drinking episode upon some event which occurs after a period of sobriety. They generally drink again, because "someone made them do it." Another defense alcoholics employ is a denial of their drinking; for if they admit they have a problem, this means acknowledgement that something is wrong which in turn presents a need for them to do something about it. They will have to seek help once acknowledgement occurs. This may be at once or it may take some time; however, they will ultimately seek some type of help. Alcoholics learn to manipulate as their addiction progresses, since it is a must to have "a bottle" available at all times. They learn to manipulate their environment, especially families and employers, in order to protect their main support, "the bottle." In group sessions, alcoholics can be stimulated to recognize these defenses and do something about them in this noncondemning atmosphere. If there is a feeling of mutual confidence between the group members, as well as with the therapist, the alcoholic will be encouraged to talk about himself and his disease, again with the goal to gain insight and understanding about his disease and, most importantly, what he can do about it!

Another type of group which is important to the treatment of the alcoholic is the small structured therapy group. After alcoholics have been participating in large group therapy sessions for at least three to four weeks, they should be assigned to a small group with one of the staff as therapist. This could be any team member, including an attendant who is trained as a lay therapist (an untrained semiprofessional who is taught group therapy techniques). Patients are selected for this small group, and again it is heterogeneous. This group is different from the large group in that it should meet once or twice a week and be composed of from five to seven patients. Generally, the meeting is held in the office of the therapist who is conducting the group, and quite frequently there are evening meetings as well as daytime sessions. In this group, discussions center around the alcoholic's feelings, life tensions, emotional traumas, relationships with family members, and his role in the community. The small group functions at a deeper level of therapy than does the large group. Timing is again important in this treatment. The therapist must be careful in his handling of material which is of a more intensive and personal nature. If this is brought up too soon in the sessions, before the alcoholics are ready, they, in turn, will be threatened to such a degree that they may lose their sobriety. Many patients could return for the small group meetings in the facility as part of their aftercare treatment following discharge. This could conceivably continue for from one to two years.

INDIVIDUAL COUNSELING

Individual counseling of alcoholics requires all the skills and tools of the professional discipline, as well as a vast knowledge of alcoholism. An individual therapist must know himself, his own attitudes and feelings towards alcohol and alcoholism. Many skilled professionals find it difficult to work with alcoholics because of their own normal bias, whether it be moralistic or cultural, since professionals are, indeed, part of our society which, in the main, condemns and rejects alcoholics. Therefore, the therapist must make a self-inventory of his own feelings and attitudes toward alcohol and alcoholism before he begins to treat alcoholics.

If the therapist is to be effective in his individual counseling of alcoholics, he must be prepared to be patient, understanding, and accepting of the alcoholic. Frequently, the patients will test out the therapist, seeking rejection by their behavior. This is a trap which must be identified by the therapist and discussed with the alcoholics. Sessions may be held on a daily, or several times a week, basis (early in the treatment) without fearing that the therapist will encounter difficulty in terminating the sessions when it is appropriate. Alcoholics, as they begin to control their drinking, learn to begin a new design for living a life without alcohol; they gain strengths and independence. Some professionals have thought it would be difficult to stop treatment, once begun, because the alcoholic, who is already dependent upon alcohol, would become too dependent upon the therapist. This is not necessarily the case. The therapist can handle this as he would any other situation. The treatment relationship can be terminated, if done so appropriately with the therapist's understanding of the alcoholic patients and their needs.

Individual therapy is not always appropriate for all alcoholics. There are some who prefer and do better, indeed, in the large group therapy sessions because they are unable to tolerate the individual relationship with a therapist which is too threatening for them. Sometimes, however, there are alcoholics who cannot accept participation in groups and respond more appropriately to individual counseling sessions. It is my experience that the therapist can help alcoholics to eventually be able to accept both types of therapy, which will give them the support and encouragement they need to maintain their sobriety.

SOCIODRAMA WITH ALCOHOLICS

An effective social therapy in the total treatment of alcoholics is sociodrama. Sociodrama, in and of itself, would not necessarily be an effective means of treatment, but in conjunction with other therapies, it augments and gives strength to the total treatment approach. In attempting to maintain sobriety, an alcoholic must learn how to live a new life, a design for living without alcohol, which brings many challenges and changes for these patients in terms of their employment, their family, their friends, and the community. Sociodrama helps alcoholics to act out some of their roles, life situations, and relationships which have proved threatening to them in the past. They learn by playing roles constructively in a therapeutic environment, as well as by observation of their fellow patients who are portraying similar roles. This "acting out of the roles" and situations, together with the discussions which follow, help them to gain some insight into self, as well as their everyday life situations.

As the sociodrama is used, it can have a therapeutic effect, not only on the patients but in their relationship with their family. As this disease has progressed, the dynamics of the family have been disrupted; the nondrinking spouse has had to assume the role of "decision maker" which, in turn, creates changes in the relationship with the alcoholic, their children, and the community. Alcoholics, through participation in sociodrama, begin to gain insight and understanding of the impact their disease has had upon their family, their employment, and the community. They learn to begin rebuilding their life with the necessary adjustments which must come, in order that they and their family can regain their place in society.

LECTURES TO ALCOHOLICS

Why, in a discussion of social therapies, is the didactic lecture included? The alcoholics are patients who must learn about their disease so that they, in turn, can learn to control their drinking. This has been found to be one of the most effective techniques of treating alcoholics. Lectures are given sequentially and provide information about alcohol and alcoholism. They include lectures concerning the effect of alcohol upon the body—the metabolism, the brain, the nervous system—and the damage which occurs as a result of the continued ingestion of alcohol by a chronic addictive alcoholic or a compulsive drinker.

Furthermore, lectures include material about alcoholism and its impact upon family, employment, industry, traffic safety, crime, and society as a whole. This is followed by lectures helping the alcoholics to learn a new way of life and gain concepts and understanding to deal with everyday problems. Most importantly, they must learn how to maintain their sobriety. Treatment personnel have learned that alcoholics need to know the danger signals which might indicate a desire to begin drinking again; these provide them with the techniques to keep them sober during the period when they want a drink. They, quite typically, go to an A.A. meeting and/or see their therapist; this helps them overcome a dangerous period and puts another building block in their road to sobriety. Families, who have been given an understanding of the disease, give strength and support to the alcoholics, as well as does the employer. Alcoholics need this type of support and encouragement when they are working to maintain this new way of life.

FILMS—ADJUNCTIVE THERAPY

Films are used in conjunction with the other treatment methods. They are considered as adjunctive therapy with the didactic lectures and the group sessions. Films provide information about the disease and its impact upon the alcoholics, their life, their family, their employment, and their community. It is another tool in helping them to understand and gain insight into their disease and to aid them toward achieving their goal of sobriety.

Some of the best films are the following: "Alcohol and the Human Body," "David: Profile of a Problem Drinker," "To Your Health," "Case 258," "Out of Orbit," and "Challenge."[4-9] Following the showing of the film, a staff member leads a discussion, which may turn into a group therapy session.

These therapies which have been described and discussed in this chapter are important as individual techniques, but have a greater effect or impact in treating alcoholics when used in a combined approach in the modified therapeutic community with the multidisciplinary team. This is considered the best available treatment for the alcoholic patients, who are suffering from an illness whose etiology is unknown, and of which there is at present no known cure. It has been found that if these social therapies are used collectively, more alcoholics respond to this type of treatment than to other types of professional treatment, as, for example, physical treatment such as aversion and/or shock therapy. Aversion therapy is a physical approach to conditioning the alcoholics so that when alcohol is ingested they become violently ill. Electric shock therapy is a treatment in which a convulsive seizure is induced by electricity. This treatment, while appropriate for specific psychiatric illness, has not been found to be helpful for the alcoholic in maintaining his sobriety.

CONCLUSION

In discussing the treatment of alcoholics, we have frequently referred to members of the multidisciplinary team, including the lay therapists who also treat the alcoholics. Regardless of whether an individual is a professional or an attendant who has been trained to be a lay therapist, it is important to consider some of the qualities which are necessary for an individual staff member to become an alcoholism therapist. First, he must have an understanding of alcohol and alcoholism; secondly, he must accept the concept that alcoholism is a treatable disease; thirdly, he must have insight into his own feelings and attitudes about alcohol and the alcoholics; fourthly, he must accept and understand the alcoholics when they appear unwilling to admit they have a disease, and recognize that they are not necessarily refusing help. The therapist must be aware that he can help alcoholics to be motivated to seek treatment earlier by his tactful handling of his first contact with the alcoholics, who initially reject help. An alcoholism therapist must have the above qualities if he is going to be able to treat the alcoholic successfully.

Alcoholics can be treated effectively to help maintain their sobriety by utilizing social therapies in an appropriate setting. In this way, the alcoholics receive the optimum in treatment available at the present time. If this treatment is provided throughout the country, it is a long way from a society whose main desire was "to keep those drunks off the streets" either by arrest, incarceration, or commitment to a mental institution. In a nation whose fourth largest public health problem is alcoholism, with some five million people affected by this disease, it would seem appropriate to make the modern day treatment techniques available to the alcoholics, rather than to neglect, punish, or jail the individuals suffering from this disease of alcoholism.

PART V

What Happens
to Alcoholics?

12

The Fate of Alcoholics:
An Evaluation of Alcoholism
Follow-Up Studies

DUFF G. GILLESPIE

INTRODUCTION

One of the few areas of agreement among students of alcoholism is that alcoholism is a social problem. There is a lack of unanimity concerning the definition of alcoholism, its etiology, the drinking pattern of alcoholics, and the effect of treatment on alcoholics—to name only a few areas of discord. This disagreement is reflected in, or is partially the result of, much of the research done in alcoholism. One of the more popular and promising types of studies employed in an attempt to fill the voids in our knowledge has been the longitudinal studies; however, the findings have been inconclusive and contradictory. The limited productivity of alcoholism follow-up studies can usually be linked with the various methodologies used by the researchers. The analysis of these research techniques is the central focus of this article.

Our evaluation includes 22 longitudinal studies drawn from a period of 20 years (1944 through 1965), and represents four disciplines (sociology, psychology, psychiatry, and internal medicine) and six countries (the United States, Canada, Fin-

REVISED version of paper presented at the 15th Annual Meeting of the Society for the Study of Social Problems, Chicago, Aug. 28–29, 1965. Supported (in part) by a Mental Health Project Grant (MH657) from the National Institute of Mental Health, United States Public Health Service.

land, Denmark, Great Britain, and the Union of South Africa).
These 22 studies include most of the published follow-up
studies for this period.

TYPES OF LONGITUDINAL STUDIES

The term, "follow-up," is the popular but often misleading
name given to three types of longitudinal studies: (1) retrospective, (2) prospective, and (3) retrospective-prospective.

Figure 1 diagrammatically illustrates the three different
types of longitudinal studies.

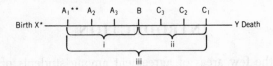

*Line X, Y, represents the career of an alcoholic.
**Letters (A through C) represent arbitrary points of time in
the alcoholic's career.

FIGURE 1.

In a retrospective study (represented by "i" in Figure 1) the
investigator collects his data by having the subject, or someone who knows the subject, recall his past. In "i," "B" represents the point in the alcoholic's life at which the researcher
attempts to collect data pertaining to the events taking place
between "A_1" and "B." Thus, retrospective studies deal only
with the alcoholic's past history.

Retrospective studies, like all longitudinal studies, attempt
to compile data which enable the researcher to develop a
pattern of crucial variables in the subject's life. Since the
principal advantage of longitudinal studies is discovering patterns of behavior in the alcoholic's life, enough of the subject's
life must be covered to allow a pattern to be discerned. However, the further the researcher goes into the subject's past,
the greater the probability that the subject may unconsciously
engage in selective recall of past events.

Of the 22 studies, only one, Lemere,[1] is retrospective.

Lemere analyzed the life histories of deceased alcoholics; he obtained his data by asking current patients to describe the life patterns of their alcoholic grandparents, parents, uncles, or aunts. Therefore, Lemere's secondary informants gave information covering up to two preceding generations. The limitation of data from secondary informants will be discussed later.

The reason for this lack of emphasis on retrospective studies can perhaps be found in the inability of researchers to establish a systematic base line. Base lines are extremely useful in ascertaining changes in a person's mode of living; as a result, most researchers have turned to approaches where base lines can be incorporated into the research design.

In a prospective study (represented by "ii" in Figure 1), the researcher ignores the events preceding his point of intervention (in this case, "B"), and he will analyze future events that occur between "B" and "C_1"; then he compares this information with the base line data collected at point "B." Follow-up interviews can be conducted at points "C_1," "C_2," and/or "C_3."

Of the remaining 21 studies, eight were prospective and used base lines to varying degrees. Ideally, base lines constitute parameters of the phenomenon under investigation and are selected on the basis of the consideration peculiar to the problem. For example, the researcher constructs an interview covering crucial variables; he then completes a prospective interview (in this case at "B") in order to establish a base line for each respondent. After a period of time (B to C_3, C_2, and/or C_1), the researcher can measure changes in the living pattern of the respondent.

One can readily see the principal limitation of the prospective longitudinal study. If the researcher desires to measure the effect which treatment, or some other intervening variable, has on the alcoholic's life, he must turn to a different approach; this approach, the retrospective-prospective study, is discussed below. Even though this limitation seems evident, seven of the eight prospective studies attempted to measure the effect of treatment on alcoholism.

In retrospective-prospective studies (represented by "iii" in

Figure 1), the researcher is concerned with events before and after the initial intervention at "B"; this is especially true if some type of treatment occurs at this point, "B," in the alcoholic's life career. As in the two previous types of studies, the researcher can choose any time period in the subject's career to analyze. For example, the researcher collects retrospective data for the time period "A_2" to "B." At point "B" the researcher also establishes a base line by means of a prospective interview. At point "C_3" the researcher conducts a follow-up interview to ascertain how the subject has changed since the base line information was collected at point "B".

Retrospective-prospective studies combine the advantages of the two previous types. By including data on the subject before he entered the study, the investigator has a built-in control for each subject. All the remaining 13 studies used this type of approach, primarily to measure the effect treatment had on the alcoholic's drinking pattern.

These diagrammatical descriptions of longitudinal studies raise several problems which limit their effectiveness. First, the researcher needs to decide how much of the alcoholic's career he will analyze. Besides the technical and fiscal problems involved in following up subjects for long time periods, there are the problems of selective recall and selective reconstruction of past events by interviewees. Too, the subject's perception of various phenomena may change through time.

One technique by which investigators try to minimize these problems is to keep the length of time the subject must recall and reconstruct as short as possible. For example, in their retrospective-prospective study, Saenger and Gerard[2] asked respondents to describe events occurring a month before intake and a month before follow-up, which was a year after discharge. But one must ask how comparable are these two time periods, for the probability that an alcoholic is drinking one month prior to treatment is much greater than a year after discharge. Also, these two time periods are a very small segment of the subject's career and, thus, may be very atypical. However, these limitations are not unique to longitudinal studies of alcoholics. Rather, they are inherent problems of longitudinal studies.

PERCENTAGE OF SAMPLES FOUND IN FOLLOW-UP STUDIES: AN OVERVIEW

No matter how much clinical experience in alcoholism the investigator has and/or how well he constructs his theoretical framework, his study is doomed to failure or, at best, mediocrity if he fails to collect sufficient follow-up data to enable him to make generalizations concerning the sample. The question is then raised: What percent of the sample must be found to enable the researcher to make valid generalizations? There is no exact percent that a researcher must strive for; some researchers may honestly feel that a follow-up consisting of 75 percent of the sample is quite adequate. However, he may also expect criticism from his colleagues. The researcher who finds 90 percent or more of the follow-up cases can feel confident that his generalizations are valid, or at least as valid as the data obtained from the subjects in the sample.

Of the 21 studies (Lemere's[1] excluded), the range on which some information was known was 38 percent to 100 percent, the latter, Davies,[3] had a sample of only seven. The median is 85 percent and the mean 81 percent. These percents appear to be quite respectable and seem to negate the contention that it is difficult to locate alcoholics for follow-up information. However, these percents represent minimal information known about the sample.

In nine of the 21 studies, the authors subdivided their follow-up cases to enable the reader to exclude such categories as: "less reliable information," "out of the community," "believed under treatment elsewhere," or "only partial data." These same authors did not use such information in their analysis, or, if they did, considered it as a separate category. Revising the percentages to exclude the above mentioned categories, we find the range of percents the same—38 percent to 100 percent. However, the median is now 77 percent and the mean is 75 percent. This is a liberal revision for only those studies whose authors stated the limitations on the "found group" were revised.

In many studies the number of subjects followed up changed from one sample characteristic to the next. For example, in one study the researchers were able to classify 78.4 percent of the sample as "improved, unchanged, or deteriorated," yet they could determine "change in interpersonal relations between intake and follow-up" for only 65.1 percent of the sample (Note 2, Tables 2 and 3). Of course, some of the variance in percent can be explained by the fact that many respondents refuse or cannot answer certain questions even under ideal conditions. But this does not explain a variance of 13 percent.

Much of this percent-located discrepancy can be explained by what can be called the "scatter gun" approach of collecting data. Of the 21 prospective and retrospective-prospective studies, 16 stated their source of data. These different sources included mailed questionnaires to patients, relatives, friends and/or the patient's doctor; personal interviews with the patients, relatives, friends, and/or the patient's doctors; telephone calls to the patient and patient's relatives, and records of other institutions and/or governmental agencies, and/or employers. Of these 16 studies, only four used personal interviews with the subject as the single source of data. Comparing the percent on which some information was obtained between the studies using the "scatter gun" approach and those only using personal interviews with the subject, we find the range for the former group to be 60 percent to 100 percent, for the latter 38 percent to 86 percent. The respective medians are 85 percent and 69 percent, the means are 85 percent and 63 percent. When the percentages are revised, using the same criteria before for the revisions, the range for the "scatter gun" approach changes to 52 percent to 100 percent; the median is lowered to 74 percent, and the mean 77 percent. Contrastingly, for the group of studies exclusively using personal interviews with subjects, the range, median, and mean remained the same.

The reasons why researchers tend to use the "scatter gun" approach can, in part, be explained by the difficulties two of the four researchers had in utilizing only personal interviews. Northcutt[4] found only 60 percent of his sample; trying to grapple with this low yield, Northcutt concluded that his main problem was the lack of adequate funds to support his study. As a result of his financial situation, he had to rely on social workers who were less than aggressive in locating the respondents.

Pfeffer and Berger believed the personal interview was the best method, but they did not undertake field interviews. They stated:[5]

One of the primary tasks was to elicit enough interest in the study so that the patients would cooperate. Requesting a former patient to return to the clinic for research purposes (providing help to himself only in a very remote way) frequently engenders little desire for participation (Note 5, p. 465).

As a result of Pfeffer and Berger's samples' disinterest in the follow-up study, the researchers found only 38 percent of all patients.

Many of the investigators using the "scatter gun" approach did so because of the reasons summarized in the following statement by Wolff and Holland:[6]

Much time would have had to be expended to trace the patients whose addresses were unknown and to obtain information about patients who did not respond to letters and telephone calls. Short of persistent visiting of patients' homes and of their neighbors and former landladies, a complete follow-up survey of a socially un-stable group of patients seems impossible to achieve. It was there-fore thought to be of interest to determine how much informa-tion could be obtained by less arduous and more practicable means . . . (Note 6, p. 114).

Earlier we saw that the "scatter gun" approach usually has a higher percentage found than the personal interview method; too, it is "less arduous and more practicable." Why, then, should not investigators use the "scatter gun" approach? There are two primary reasons. Firstly, alcoholism is still viewed negatively by a substantial segment of the population. As a result, many alcoholics would rather their friends and relatives not know of their condition. This right should be respected by the researcher and the safest way of doing this is by not asking the patients' relatives and friends about the subjects' alcoholism.

Secondly, Guze *et al.*,[7] have shown that relatives are not always accurate in describing an alcoholic relative's condition. His study, in which the alcoholics and their relatives were given the identical interviews, found that the two groups disagreed on 26 percent of the answers; the diagnosis of alcoholism could be made from the responses of the alcoholic in 97 percent of the cases. Contrastingly, the diagnosis could be made from the responses of the relatives in only 41 percent of the cases. The reason for this divergence was due to the relatives' ignorance of the alcoholic's condition, or a reflection of their moralistic views toward alcoholism from which they tried to protect their family's reputation. Because of the unreliability of data acquired from relatives, the only condition under which the researcher should resort to interviewing relatives for primary data is when the subject is known to be deceased. Although data from relatives can be useful as a supplement to the patient's data, this should be done only with the consent of the patient.

Thus, the three principal defects in the "scatter gun" technique of follow-up are: (1) Much of the information derived from secondary sources is only fragmentary and cannot be used throughout the analysis; (2) the ethical problem of possibly exposing the alcoholic's condition to friends, relatives, or even employers; and (3) the accuracy of secondary data is problematic because the respondents do not always know the subject's condition or they perceive it in a distorted manner.

The two principal drawbacks of the personal interview approach are: (1) It requires large expenditures of money and time, and (2) the alcoholic is sometimes uncooperative. The reasons for these two drawbacks can be explained by describing the sample characteristics of the 22 longitudinal studies.

CHARACTERISTICS OF ALCOHOLICS WHICH AFFECT THE VALIDITY OF LONGITUDINAL STUDIES

It is difficult to construct a demographic profile of all the samples in these studies because of lack of uniformity of data collected by the researchers. Still, a limited description of the populations studied is possible.

These samples, excluding Lemere,[1] were taken from public institutions. Thus, the populations are most likely drawn from the lower and lower-middle social classes. Limited data support this contention to some degree. Of the 21 studies, 13 presented data from which social class could be discerned with some accuracy. Using a six-class scale, ranging from upper-upper to lower-lower, the breakdown was as follows: Six of the studies consisted largely of upper-middle and lower-middle patients, two of lower-middle class, two of lower-middle and upper-lower, two of upper-lower, and one of upper-lower and lower-lower. Therefore, of the 13 studies which gave social class information there were only three which were predominantly lower-class. However, the social class data did not always take social status decline into consideration.

By examining other variables, we can learn more of the alcoholics' economic and social resources. Nine studies gave the employment status of the sample at intake. The range of the percent unemployed was 27 to 81 percent; the median was 52 percent and the mean was 48 percent. Of six studies which gave information on the arrest record of their samples at intake, the range of previous arrests was 27 percent to 100 percent, the median was 35 percent, and the mean 45 percent. Thirteen studies gave marital status data at intake. The range of divorced or separated individuals was 18 percent to 55 percent; the median was 32 percent; and the mean was 35 percent. Five of the studies gave data stating what portion of their sample was known to have been residents of other communities than that in which their intake interview was completed; the range was from 7 to 27 percent; the median was 11 percent, and the mean was 15 percent. Thus, the alcoholics studied are characterized by meager economic resources, their inability to maintain a successful spouse relationship, a high risk rate for arrest, and a tendency to migrate from one community to another.

As a result of these characteristics, the typical alcoholic in these studies is not easy to locate for a follow-up interview.

He undoubtedly has difficulties paying rent and other debts which may have a two-fold effect; he is very likely to move or be evicted, and when he does move, he is unlikely to leave a forwarding address (and why should he when the people most likely to want to find him are bill collectors, the police, or an ex-wife seeking alimony).

Another characteristic of alcoholics that presents a methodological problem is the alcoholic's high mortality rate. Fifteen of the studies have the mortality rate of their samples. The range was from 2 to 19 percent. The median was 7 percent, and the mean was 8 percent. Typically, the researchers ended the follow-up investigation of a subject as soon as they learned of his death. An exception was Lipscomb[8] who was primarily interested in the mortality rate and causes of death among alcoholics. He was able to give the cause of death for all of the known deceased alcoholics in his sample. Lipscomb relied heavily on State Health Department Registries as a tool for learning about deaths. The use of such governmental sources, supplemented by interviews with relatives, should enable future investigators to fill this serious gap in our knowledge of alcoholism.

OTHER METHODOLOGICAL PROBLEMS

Of the 22 studies, all but two (Lemere[1] and Lipscomb[8]) tried to measure the effect of treatment on the alcoholic cases. It was stated earlier that the retrospective-prospective longitudinal study was the best type of approach since it enables the researcher to compare crucial variables before and after treatment. Still, seven prospective studies (Wolff and Holland,[6] Norvig and Nielsen,[9] Wallerstein,[10] Cowen,[11] Hoff and McKeown,[12] Prout, et al.,[13] and Wall and Allen[14]) attempted to measure the effect of treatment on their samples. In most cases the sole criterion for improvement was the subject's drinking pattern, for it was not possible to measure changes in other variables (such as living conditions and employment status) since they did know the subject's status before treatment. However, this point raises another question: How does the investigator measure improvement in the patient's drinking pattern if he cannot compare the pattern before and after treatment? As seen earlier in this article, one way to cope with this dilemma is to have only two drinking categories—drinking and abstinent. Only one study (Wolff and Holland[6]) used such a classification; and although they might be able to state that abstinent patients have improved in their drinking patterns (at least during the period of follow-up) they can say little more about their sample. The other six studies used such categories as "good," "fair," and "poor," or "still drinking," "unimproved," "drinking, but managing better," and "recovered." The reader has no way of ascertaining how these categories were developed, rather he must assume that these on the surface subjective evaluations of the investigator are consistent and valid. An interesting point is that in all seven studies, the principal investigator was either an internist or a psychiatrist. A heartening point is that six of the seven investigations were done before 1957, which may indicate that prospective studies are no longer viewed as a useful research tool for measuring the effect of treatment.

There is a trend toward the exclusive use of the retrospective-prospective study and the use of variables in addition to drinking pattern in measuring changes in alcoholism longitudinal studies. All but one of the retrospective-prospective studies were after 1956, and all but two of the 13 included variables for analysis other than the drinking pattern of the alcoholic. Furthermore, since 1960, all longitudinal studies (there have been nine) have been retrospective-prospective and have included factors other than drinking status in their follow-up analysis. In short, current investigators appear to have accepted the contention that improvement is a multi-dimensional phenomenon based on how well the subject functions in the society and is not solely dependent on his drinking pattern.

As a result of the above contention, some students of alcoholism believe certain alcoholics can return to normal drinking. Several studies briefly mentioned that part of their sample appeared to adopt a normal drinking pattern. However, it was not until Davies'[3] study in 1962 that the question of an alcoholic's drinking normally became a seriously and much discussed question. Davies followed up seven men from seven to 11 years and considered them to be normal drinkers. It is beyond this article's scope to discuss this problem in any detail.

One of the inherent flaws in a follow-up study is that the investigator can cover only a segment of the alcoholic's career. In other words, the researcher may perceive what he considers normal drinking for a seemingly substantial part of the alcoholic's life. Yet, he cannot unequivocally state that the alcoholic will not have a serious relapse later in life. Of course, such questions have been raised before and were countered many times by a finding of Lemere's. Lemere stated, "In 49, or 10 percent [of sample], the drinking gradually moderated until, at the time of their death, it had not been a serious problem for many years" (Note 1, p. 674). Of course, what relatives perceive as a "serious problem" among their antecedents may be seen in a different light by a clinician. Moreover, Lemere states, "Thirty-eight, or 8 percent [of the sample] had histories of having stopped drinking for three years or longer only to relapse at some later date. These relapses, after long periods of abstinence point out how meaningless are evaluations of treatment based on follow-up studies of only a few months or a year or two" (Note 1, p. 675). It is true that follow-up studies usually cannot measure the final outcome of treated alcoholics; however, to say they are "meaningless" is too harsh a judgment.

One way in which the measurement of the effect treatment may have on alcoholics is through the use of control groups. Four of the studies used control groups to measure the effects different types of treatment had on alcoholics. However, only Bruun's study[19] had a precise methodology. By utilizing an untreated control group, or a control group treated differently, the investigator can at least learn if treatment or what type of treatment has immediate positive effects in his sample. If, for example, the researcher finds that the untreated control group's outcome was much worse than the treated study group, he can assume that the treatment had some positive effect on his study group.

Many researchers have tried to establish what length of follow-up is most desirable for measuring the outcome of treated alcoholics. Gerard and Saenger[15] concluded that most alcoholics who relapse during the follow-up will do so in the first year (which appears to be the case with studies that included this information), and, therefore, a one-year follow-up does not distort the patient's outcome to any great degree. Still, this method does not take into consideration those patients who relapse after the follow-up study has ended. It may be some time before we learn what time period of follow-up (within technical and economic limitations) is best suited for follow-up. So far, the studies have shown no particular favor for any specific time length of follow-up. The minimum time of follow-up could be discerned in 15 studies. The range was three months to seven years, the median and mean were 23 months. The range of maximum time for follow-up in the 21 studies (Lemere's[1] excluded) was 12 to 134 months, with a median of 36 and a mean of 55 months. Despite the questionable importance of learning the "ideal" follow-up period, it is obvious that the longer a researcher can follow up his sample, the greater the chance that he will learn of changes in the alcoholic's life.

The primary purpose of alcoholism longitudinal studies need not be the measurement of treatment effect, but rather to facilitate our understanding of the phenomenon by showing us how a multitude of factors affect the alcoholic. Indeed, the researcher's entry into the alcoholic's career at a treatment facility may be viewed as just a convenient point of intervention. If the researcher is less concerned with the effect of treatment, the length of follow-up decreases in importance.

It is true that a researcher may have little choice in determining what type of person will be in his sample. Instead, he must study the individual who happens to be in the treatment facility during his research. Still, he should attempt not to bias his sample toward any group or type of individual. In 10 of the 22 studies, some form of screening process took place. The type of screening ranged from allowing only "voluntary" patients in the study [Hoff and McKeown[12]] to the more extensive screening process of Moore and Ramseur[16] or Davies, *et al.*[17] Moore and Ramseur's selection of patients aimed ". . . toward accepting for admission those patients who appear to have a more favorable prognosis and who will accept psychotherapy as a means of alleviating their difficulty." Moore and Ramseur concluded that "this tends to exclude alcoholics who are deteriorated, psychotic, or of limited intelligence" (Note 16, p. 234). Davies excluded "any patient who declined help and did not wish to give up drinking . . . Others who were excluded were those who showed dementia, or whose alcohol addiction was not their central problem (as, for example, in some psychopaths who were also perverts, drug addicts, pathological liars and swindlers)" (Note 17, p. 486). Such selection procedures have a two-fold effect. First, they distort the samples in such a manner that the samples no longer represent the alcoholic population that originally came in contact with the treatment facilities. For example, one of the alcoholic types Davies excluded was "drug addicts." Recent literature in England suggests that the use of alcohol, barbiturates, and/or amphetamines is not uncommon in that country, especially among middle-aged women. Second, by excluding alcoholic types which are characterized by their instability, the researcher is more likely to have a sample which is easier to locate. The average percent of subjects located for the ten studies which used a screening process was 87 percent. The corresponding figure for the 11 which did not screen their sample was 75 percent.

Recalling the earlier discussion concerning the social class found in the studies, one is aware that the two extremes of social status are missing, namely, the upper-upper class and lower-upper and the lower-lower class. Only Mindlin's[18] sample had a significant number of lower-lower class individuals. Rather, the studies' samples, on the whole, seem to be made up of lower-middle class alcoholics. Thus, one of the country's largest social problem groups, the chronic police case inebriate (commonly called "revolving door" alcoholics), has not been analyzed by longitudinal studies. Besides these alcoholics, another group is conspicuously missing from these evaluations—the Negro. This exclusion is extremely important, since there is some evidence that Negroes deviate from the Gamma type of alcoholism which characterizes the American alcoholic. Pittman has suggested that Negroes fall into the Delta type of alcoholic in Jellinek's scheme of classification of alcoholism.

SUMMARY

This analysis of 22 longitudinal studies has shown that of the three types of studies (retrospective, prospective, and retrospective-prospective), the retrospective-prospective is currently the most frequently used because of its ability to measure the changes that take place in the sample before and after treatment. It was suggested that the type of base line that the researcher employs is influenced by his training and interest, and that the use of base lines is essential for adequate longitudinal studies.

Longitudinal studies have certain limitations such as their inability to cover only a relatively short period of the alcoholic's career and the fact that respondents may engage in selective recall and reconstruction. These inherent limitations make the longitudinal study a difficult tool to use in measuring the effect of treatment on an alcoholic's career. The measurement of treatment effect can be facilitated by utilizing control groups.

Personal interviews are expensive and difficult, but yield more accurate data than that collected from secondary sources. However, most studies collected data from secondary sources because alcoholics have high rates of marital instability, unemployment, arrest, and geographic mobility. Longitudinal studies are a crucial research tool because of their ability to discern the multitude of factors which affect alcoholics. However, in order to accurately represent the general alcoholic population, researchers should refrain from screening their samples and concentrate on alcoholic groups which are currently under-represented in the literature, namely, the upper-upper class, the lower-lower class, and Negroes.

13

Measures of Treatment Outcome
for Alcoholics:
A Model of Analysis

SARAH LEE BOGGS

APPROACHES TO THE EVALUATION
OF TREATMENT OUTCOME

Over the past few years, much interest has been shown in
the evaluation of outcome of persons released from alcoholism
treatment programs as evidenced by the plethora of studies
dealing with this topic (see Gillespie, Chapter 12). On the
whole, these previous studies have failed to produce clear
and systematic findings so that any one approach can be repli-
cated, or the results from one study adequately compared
with those from any others.

The inconsistent findings from these follow-up studies can
be attributed to inadequate research orientations and methods
that characterize much of the work that has been done. Subjective and unspecified evaluation criteria, incomplete and
irregular sampling procedures, untested levels of significance
between outcome groups are examples of the deficiencies
that appear in these studies. Increasing recognition has been
given to these problems, and in the work of Mindlin,[1] Gibbins
and Armstrong,[2] and Williams,[3] findings are presented that
are based on systematic and objective methods of analysis.

The study that is reported here is a further endeavor to
improve on the measurement of the effects of alcoholism treatment programs. Using the Guttman scaling technique,[4] a

SUPPORTED by a Mental Health Project Grant (MH–657) from the
National Institute of Mental Health, United States Public Health
Service.

drinking scale is applied to the drinking levels reported by a group of alcoholics before and after treatment.

This approach has many advantages over the less rigorous subjective evaluations that have been made in the past. For one, this method allows for a systematic comparison to be made of individuals according to their relative position or ranking on the drinking scale. Also it enables a comparison to be made of individuals before and after treatment by their change in scale position or rank. Of particular importance is the fact that the scale clearly indicates the nature of the items that are incorporated in the rating scheme, and identifies the particular items that are relevant to the content areas that are being measured.

The problem with much of the work that has been carried out in previous follow-up studies of treated alcoholics is not one of the "subjectivity" of the items that are being measured, but rather of the subjectivity of the methods that have been employed by the investigators to measure the outcome of treatment. Motivation on the part of an alcoholic patient as shown by Mindlin,[1] and the degree of social integration as shown by Gibbins and Armstrong[2] are important variables that are significantly related to treatment outcome. These so-called "soft" data are crucial to the assessment of outcome, and are shown to be much more relevant to evaluation than the more objective or "hard" data such as the number of hospitalizations or length of treatment exposure. These latter variables are frequently reported to have little relationship to outcome of treatment.[2, 5, 6]

The point at issue here is that the investigators themselves employ subjective measures in the evaluation process, for there is no clear specification of the items and the ratings that are used as the basis for assessing outcome. The use of categories like "stable, usually stable, and quite unstable" work histories of patients,[7] or the ratings of "good, fair, and poor" personal attachment levels[8] are examples of the inadequacies that pervade many of these rating schemes based on the judgments of clinicians and investigators. The problems are inextricably compounded when these non-specified evaluations of numerous content areas are pooled together into an over-all evaluation of "cured, changed, and unchanged" drinking patterns, or "very successful, somewhat successful, and unsuccessful" treatment outcomes.

This is not to say that therapists' attitudes and perspectives, like those of the patients as explained above, are not important data in and of themselves. The issue hinges on the fact that the evaluation should be analytically separated from the ratings, rather than being directly incorporated within the measurement schemes themselves. The work of Pittman and Sterne[9] on the impact of attitudes of treatment personnel and community agency administrators toward alcoholics indicates the importance of this kind of variable on the development of and referral to community alcoholism treatment programs. Hollingshead and Redlich's classic study[10] of the consequences for treatment and treatment response depending upon the social class levels of patients and psychiatrists is further evidence of the independent contribution to outcome that the clinicians' judgments make.

Another major variant in follow-up studies of treated alcoholics is the content areas that are evaluated before and after treatment. Some studies rely exclusively upon the drinking patterns of persons after release as the single criterion for evaluating treatment outcome, but most investigators recognize that drinking behavior is only one among several behavioral characteristics necessary to take into consideration for an adequate appraisal of the eventual social adjustment attained by the treated alcoholics.

In this study, the level of social functioning of the patients before and after treatment will be assessed with respect to work status and occupation, social stability and community integration, health status, institutionalization, and legal conforming behavior. The research reported here is limited to the area of drinking levels before and after treatment, but future work will be done on the other areas of social functioning employing the same methodological framework of developing valid scales and relating these scales to other variables such as race, sex, and age.

Which variables are taken as independent (causal) and which are taken as dependent (effect) is another latent and varying aspect of alcoholism follow-up research. In many research models, the causal chain of events is not specified, but the implicit assumption that seems to underlie the work is that drinking is the primary causative factor in producing problems in other areas of social life.

The orientation underlying this study, however, is that drinking behavior is only one interdependent element in the integrated social functioning of each particular individual. Therefore, change in any one element of the composite whole creates change in other parts. Thus, under some conditions, heavy drinking precedes job loss and drinking may be taken as the causal variable, whereas under other conditions, heavy drinking is resumed at the loss of a job, so in this case drinking is seen as the effect variable. In another instance, a family is dissolved because of the heavy drinking of one member, while in other cases, this member's heavy drinking is resumed at the time the family is disrupted. The analytic model of interdependent elements used here makes explicit the absence of a known ordering of variables.

The Treatment Program and the Sample

The work that is reported here is based on a sample of cases that were selected from all persons who, during a two and one-half year period, were admitted to an alcoholism treatment facility at a municipal psychiatric hospital in the City of St. Louis.[11] The requirements for conducting this comparative study of two different approaches to the treatment of alcoholism were introduced at the initial establishment of the treatment facility and were an integral part of the facility from its beginning. Thus, from its inception, the program was designed to incorporate the evaluative research into the routine operations.

The purpose of the study is to evaluate the effectiveness of two different types of alcoholism treatment programs by assessing the outcomes of persons who received the different treatments. The research design was the classic experimental type such that at admission there were no differences between the two groups, and at outcome, the two groups can be compared with respect to differences in the adequacy of their social functioning.

The "control" group members were given the standard "drying out" routines that are administered to alcoholics treated in general hospitals. These consist of the treatment of the effects of acute intoxication, and require from three to seven days of in-patient care.

The "experimental" group, or study patients, were given a more extensive and diversified regimen, consisting of medical, psychiatric, social casework treatment, group therapy, didactic lectures, and occupational therapy, in addition to the initial detoxification treatment. After receiving from three to six weeks of in-patient care, as compared with one week for the control cases, the experimental group members could continue to have contact with the treatment staff, return to participate in an Alcoholics Anonymous group established by the patients in the treatment center, and were referred by the staff to appropriate social agencies in the community when this was needed. Thus, the control program was basically limited to the treatment of the physical aspects of the illness while the experimental program was concerned with treating not only the physical aspects, but the psychological and social implications as well.

Beginning in February, 1962, and for the two and one-half years that the study was in progress, 1006 different persons were admitted to the treatment facility. The majority of these persons had admitted themselves to the hospital, and about the same proportions had been brought in by friends or relatives as had been brought in by the police.

The medical residents in attendance in the admitting room of the general hospital decided if the psychiatric residents on duty at the adjoining psychiatric hospital should be consulted on the question of whether or not to admit the person to the alcoholism treatment unit. Since the medical personnel changed periodically throughout the course of the study, the policies and practices that were followed in admitting persons to the unit were subject to some variations in interpretations from time to time by the different admitting officers.

Despite this source of definitional variation, there is little question that all the persons admitted to the treatment facility had severe drinking problems.

From the group of 1006 persons who were admitted to the alcoholism treatment unit, 255 individuals were selected to participate in the study, or approximately one out of every four persons admitted to the treatment facility. The selection of study participants from among all the patients admitted was determined through a staff conference attended by the alcoholism treatment unit's nurses, psychiatrists, internist, and psychiatric social workers.

Five pre-set criteria guided the staff's decision regarding the individual patient's eligibility for participation in the evaluation study. The purpose of these criteria was to select persons who had some chance for returning to the community without some severe physical or social handicap that would seriously interfere with his adjustment, regardless of the treatment that had been received in the experimental program. This orientation is reflected in the following criteria that were used for selection of study participants.

I. Criteria for absolute exclusion from long-term care program:
   Progressive or markedly debilitating (1) medical disease, for example, active tuberculosis, terminal cancer, severe liver cirrhosis, or (2) psychiatric disease, for example, severe obsessive-compulsive neurosis, nuclear schizophrenia, severe chronic brain syndrome.
II. Criteria for permissive acceptance of patients for long-term care program: (Patient must possess at least one criterion to be considered for long-term care).
   A. Married, living with spouse, or living with family members, or friend in a familial relationship to which they can return.
   B. Steady job for two or more years in last 10 years.
   C. Referral: self (sober, not under legal duress or homeless); or by family; or agency (A.A., social agency or physician).

D. Regular or steady job available after discharge or
possesses training and/or experience for semi-
skilled or better jobs.

If the patient was not seriously impaired by physical or
psychiatric disease, could meet one of the four socio-economic
requirements, and agreed to take part in the study by con-
senting to stay in the facility for three or more weeks if necessary, a pre-established random selection procedure was followed to determine whether the person would be placed in
the "experimental" group or in the "control" group. Of the
255 participants in the evaluation study, 184 (or 72.2 percent)
were randomly assigned to the "study" group, and 71 (or
27.8 percent) were assigned to the "control" group.

In brief, the sample was composed primarily of unattached,
working-class, white males in their middle adult years. Specifically, 88.4 percent of the sample were males; 80.5 percent
were white; 75.7 percent were either single, widowed,
separated, or divorced; 41.1 median years of age; 10.7 median
years of school completed; and $38.30 median weekly income
for the three months prior to their admission to the hospital.

At the time of admission to the treatment program after
the persons had recovered from the effects of acute intoxication, a battery of questionnaires was administered. The information gathered consisted of extensive data regarding
facets of the patient's background such as work history, drinking history, previous physical and psychiatric symptoms,
institutionalization, family and marital history, arrest and
incarceration history, transiency and residency patterns, armed
services record, etc. As soon as the person had been placed
on the evaluation study, a record was kept of all subsequent
re-admissions to the treatment facility.

At one year after the person's initial discharge from the
treatment facility, the follow-up effort was begun. Of the
total 255 persons included in the evaluation study, 241 or 95
percent were located. As discussed by Gillespie, this is the
highest number of follow-up subjects located and interviewed.

A frequent practice used in many follow-up studies is to
obtain information about the respondent from a secondary

source, especially from relatives. The necessity of getting the information directly from the patient rather than from another source has been documented in a methodological study in which the reports of alcoholics and their relatives are compared.[12] These authors found that "the diagnosis of alcoholism could be made from the responses of the subject alone in 97 percent of the 39 alcoholics. It could be made from the responses of the relatives in only 41 percent of the alcoholics."

In all but two of the cases in this study, a follow-up interview was conducted with the respondents themselves. One exception to this was an individual who had left the community and was living in a distant state. A follow-up interview was held with the respondent's mother who reported that the patient was still drinking heavily. The other individual was one who had been found dead on the street, and whose only living relative resided in another state. These persons had maintained no contact with each other for many years, and the surviving relative did not appear at the inquest or the funeral. Thus, it was decided that a follow-up interview with this relative would provide little if any information about the respondent's post-hospital adjustment. All in all, interview information was obtained for 240 persons.

The 95 percent location rate indicates the efforts that were put into finding all the participants in the evaluation study. At the time of follow-up, 212 (or 88.3 percent) of the respondents were living in the local community, while 11 (or 4.6 percent) were found elsewhere in the metropolitan area or state, and 17 (or 7.1 percent) were living in other states.

A severe limitation of many follow-up studies, and especially problematic in retrospective ones, is the proportion of persons who are never located or who do not respond to the inquiry that is made regarding their follow-up status. The nonresponse rate has ranged as high as 40 percent in some of these studies. This result raises the question of the degree to which the findings from such studies are biased by these nonreported cases. Are the missing cases ones whose outcomes are the worst, or the ones who have done the best? In addition to the proportions who refuse to respond in any sample of a normal population, a deviant group like the one studied here has special reason to refuse out of the desire to avoid any reminder of their problem with alcohol that the follow-up inquiry might represent.

A further problem that may distort the conclusions of follow-up studies has to do with maintaining the ratios of experimental to control cases. It is thought that control cases are more difficult to locate because they are the ones who would be expected to be doing poorly. Also, it is the control cases who may be more difficult to gain cooperation from because they have less investment in the treatment program. An over-representation of study cases in the final sample could seriously distort the over-all conclusions in the direction of successful outcomes.

Particular effort was exerted in this study to prevent the occurrence of these sources of bias. The ratio of study and control cases was maintained throughout the course of the research so that the final ratios would be the same as those that had been predetermined by random procedures at the beginning of the study. The degree to which this was accomplished is shown by the close similarity between the initial and final ratios in the study reported in Table 1.

TABLE 1.   Distribution of Interviewed and Not Interviewed
Study and Control Cases

Treatment Group	Located and Interviewed		Not Located or Not Interviewed		Total	
	No.	%	No.	%	No.	%
Study	173	72.1	11	73.3	184	72.2
Control	67	27.9	4	26.7	71	27.8
TOTAL	240	100.0	15	100.0	255	100.0

Follow-Up Interview

When the persons had been located, a follow-up interview was conducted with them. The majority of these cases were interviewed in the field, that is 208 (or 86.6 percent). Sixteen (or 6.7 percent) of the respondents were interviewed in the treatment center during a re-admission on or about a year after their initial discharge, and another 16 (6.7 percent) came into the hospital or an agency for an interview. It was found that the respondents were much more likely to comply with the request for an interview if the staff came to their homes or other designated place than if they were asked to come into the hospital or a social agency.

The length of the follow-up period covered in the study for the 241 individuals ranged from nine to 32 months, the median period being 13.2 months between initial hospital discharge and follow-up interview.

The follow-up questionnaire incorporated questions relating to the period after the person's initial discharge from the treatment program, and inquiry was made into the person's drinking patterns, work history, arrest history and incarcerations, marital and family stability, mobility and residency patterns, health status and treatment, institutionalization, formal and informal social participation, and the person's own perceptions of how well he was doing in comparison with the period prior to entering the treatment program.

DRINKING SCALES

A variety of questions pertaining to the drinking patterns of the respondents was asked in the In-take and the Follow-up questionnaires. Five questions relating to the level of drinking were selected for the drinking scale analysis, matched for their inclusion in both sets of questionnaires. These questions measured the frequency with which the person drank; the amount of drinking, that is, whether he usually drank to intoxication; work or job loss from drinking; whether treatment was required for his drinking; and whether there had been periods during which the person had not drunk, and if so, how long these periods lasted.

Detailed answers were given to each of these questions, but for scaling purposes, the answer categories were dichotomized so that each case was given a score of "0" or "1" with the higher score indicating a greater amount of drinking.

One-hundred cases out of the total sample of 241 were used

for a pilot test to determine whether a drinking scale could be devised, and if so, whether this method of analysis was useful enough to warrant applying it to the entire sample of cases. The data and findings reported in the following sections are the results of this pilot test.

In-Take Drinking Scale

In order to set up a scalogram for the scaling analysis, the individual questions must be arranged so that the first item is the one that has the largest number of "positive" responses. Positive responses in this drinking scale are those that reflect the greatest amount of drinking, and are the ones that are scored "1." For the in-take drinking scale, the questions were scored and ordered in the manner presented in the list below.

For the next step in the scaling process, the cases are ar-

LIST OF IN-TAKE DRINKING SCALE ITEMS

Scale Items	Score 0	Score 1
1. Have you ever been drunk?	No	Yes
2. During the last year, how many days did you lose from work because of drinking?	Worked, with no days lost because of drinking.	Did not work, or lost days from work because of drinking.
3. Have you had previous treatment or hospitalization for drinking?	No	Yes
4. What has your drinking pattern been like over the past three months?	Aperiodic, periodic	Steady
5. How long was your longest dry period during the last year?	One month or more.	Less than one month.

ranged in descending order according to their total scores, starting with the cases having scores of five, and ending with the cases having scores of zero. To the extent that the individual items in the scale are internally consistent, and indeed do form a scale, an individual's total score will predict his score on each separate item within the scale. Thus, a score of five will indicate that the individual case had a positive response to all five items in the scale; a score of four will indicate that the case had a positive response to the first four items, and a negative response to the fifth one; and so on.

The following description characterizes the response patterns for each of the five perfect scale types on the in-take drinking scale.

DESCRIPTION OF PERFECT IN-TAKE SCALE TYPES

Scale score	*Description*
5	Has been drunk; did not work, or lost days from work because of drinking during past year; has had previous treatment for drinking; has drunk steadily over past three months; had less than one month dry period during past year.
4	Has been drunk; did not work, or lost days from work because of drinking during past year; has had previous treatment for drinking; has drunk steadily during past three months; had dry period of at least one month during last year.
3	Has been drunk; did not work, or lost days from work because of drinking during past year; has had previous treatment for drinking; has drunk, but only periodically (less than steady) during past three months; had dry period of at least one month during past year.
2	Has been drunk; did not work, or lost days from work because of drinking during past year; has not had previous treatment for drinking; has drunk, but only periodically (less than steady) during past three months; had dry period of at least one month during past year.
1	Has been drunk; worked with no days lost because of drinking during past year; has not had previous treatment for drinking; has drunk, but only peri-

odically (less than steady) during past three months;
had dry period of at least one month during past
year.

o   Has never been drunk; worked with no days lost
because of drinking during past year; has not had
previous treatment for drinking; has drunk, but only
periodically (less than steady) during past three
months; had dry period of at least one month during past year.

The in-take drinking scale yielded a coefficient of reproducibility of 0.87, which is only slightly lower than the .90
level suggested as the cutting point between a scale and a
quasi-scale. Since this is a pilot test in which only 100 cases
have been used, and the coefficient is very close to the accepted level, no further efforts were made to improve the
scale even though there are several possible alternatives that
could be pursued. When more cases are included in the
analysis, it is very likely that the coefficient will be increased.

When the cases are scored in the designated manner, the
distribution of drinking scores at admission to the treatment
program, as presented in Table 2, show that the modal type
among these 100 cases had a score of three, and a median
score of 3.3. This indicates that at admission to the treatment
program, over one-half of the patients were well advanced
in the progressive debilitating sequence of alcoholism. For
95 percent of these persons (scores of two or more on the
scale) drinking not only was heavy and continuous, but it had
progressed to the point where it was interfering with carrying out their work responsibilities. For only five percent of
these persons at admission to the program did heavy drinking
occur without disruption of their jobs. From these data, it
appears that within this population stratum, drinking to the
extent that hospital treatment is considered necessary means
that the individual is experiencing severe physical, psychological, and social consequences as a result of his drinking.
Not until this point does the individual himself or society in
the role of the police, clergy, friends, and relatives define the
situation as serious enough to take action and seek hospital
treatment.

TABLE 2. Distribution of In-Take Drinking Scale Scorce

Scale Score	Frequency	Per Cent
0	0	. . .
1	5	5.0
2	16	16.0
3	43	43.0
4	29	29.0
5	7	7.0
TOTAL	100	100.0

A verbal description summarizing the drinking behavior and history of the persons characterized by different scale types provides a detailed version of the more concise and objective descriptions from the scale. The case summaries below describe the typical type of patient at admission in contrast to the extreme types, the maximum score of five and the lowest admission score of one.

Scale score three. The patient indicates that prior to admission, he had been drinking heavily for four days. He states that as a result of his drinking, he was shaking badly and was vomiting. He feared that he was going into DT's. In the presence of these symptoms, he felt that he was unable to work, and did not know whether he would be able to stop drinking. The patient decided to admit himself to the hospital. He had heard from AA members that there was an alcoholism treatment center, and as a result he presented himself to the admitting room of the hospital where he was subsequently admitted.

The patient stated that he first started drinking at about age 15, but he could not remember when he first got drunk. He reported that his heavy drinking really started while he was in the Service in the 1940s, even though he was only drinking heavily on a periodic basis at that time. He first started experiencing morning shakes while he was in the Service, but he does not remember when he first began taking morning drinks. He first had blackouts about a year and a half ago, and DT's for the first time a little more than a year ago.

The patient describes his longest binge as lasting from two and one-half to three months. His longest dry period was about four months, occurring approximately a year ago. He was able to stay dry this length of time with the aid of Antabuse.

Since the early 1960s, the patient has had many jobs, moving around the country a good deal, and being fired because of his drinking. Prior to admission, he was working as a kitchen laborer for a few weeks, and was fired from this job because of his drinking.

He had received previous treatment for alcoholism during a 72-day stay at a public hospital in another state.

To compare the average type of patient at admission, the following is an excerpt from a case summary of a patient characterized by a score of five, or the maximum possible drinking score.

Scale score five: The patient stated that he had been drinking regularly over a prolonged period of time and on a daily basis. He stated that his purpose for being on the treatment unit was due to his fear of going into DT's. As a result, he came to the hospital for help and was subsequently admitted.

The patient describes himself as experiencing his first drink when he was very young, but did not remember his exact age when this occurred. He reported that his first drunk took place when he was twelve years old.

Since his discharge from the Service in the mid-1950s, he has held only two jobs, the longest one lasting about ten months from which he was fired for drinking. Currently his income is derived from running errands for people in his neighborhood in order to get whatever change he can so that he can buy himself a bottle of wine. The longest period of abstinence he has experienced was one month when he stopped drinking out of fear of having DT's.

By contrast, the following is a description of a person of scale type one, the lowest score at admission among these cases.

Scale score one: The patient said that prior to his admission, he was drinking for about a week. He is a clerk in an office where his work is dependent upon the presence of his supervisor. The supervisor had been away from the office for some time, so that the patient found himself with a lot of free time, and he felt that this lent itself to his increased drinking. He presented himself at the admitting room of the hospital as he thought he needed help and would not be able to stop drinking on his own.

The patient stated that his first drink occurred in his teens, but he could not recall the exact incident. His first drunk was at the age of 15 years. He had experienced morning shakes about ten years ago at the age of 22, and has never taken morning drinks as he would rather go through whatever discomfort he has to experience than start drinking when he first gets up in the morning. He first began experiencing blackouts when he was about 25 years old, and never has had DT's. His longest binge lasted for a matter of four or five days, and this started only within the last two years. He has tried to stop drinking every time he gets drunk, but he has never been able to refrain from drinking for more than one or two months at a time.

Through personal contacts, the patient had gotten a job as a clerk in an office where he had been continuously employed for the past three years.

These cases illustrate the extent of drinking by the persons at different levels on the drinking scale. These case summaries clearly show that the higher scale scores measure greater intensities of drinking.

Follow-Up Drinking Scale

On the basis of the largest number of positive responses to the questions, the ordering of the items in the follow-up drinking scale was changed from that of the in-take drinking scale, but the items and the scoring patterns remained the same.

The follow-up drinking scale yielded a coefficient of reproducibility of 0.90, clearly indicating the validity of these five items in measuring drinking intensity. The median drinking score at follow-up for these 100 cases was 4.2, and the modal score was five.

LIST OF FOLLOW-UP DRINKING SCALE ITEMS

Scale items	Score 0	Score 1
1. Have you been drinking since leaving the Unit, and if so, how often?	Not drinking	Any drinking: from "less than once a month," to "almost every day or steady."
2. How long has your longest dry period been since leaving the Unit?	Twelve months or more	Less than twelve months
3. Have you had any treatment for drinking since leaving the Unit?	No treatment needed	Some treatment needed

| 4. Have you been intoxicated since your discharge, and if so, how often? | Never intoxicated | Any intoxication: from "less than once a month," to "several times a week." |
| 5. How many days did you lose from work because of drinking, and did you lose any jobs? | Worked, and no days or jobs lost because of drinking | Never worked, or lost days or jobs because of drinking |

Several reasons can be advanced to explain the large number of cases who at follow-up had the maximum drinking scores. First, there is the fact that most of these persons were well advanced in the sequence of alcoholism at the time they were admitted to the program. That is, more than one out of every three of these persons had drinking scores of four or five at the time they were admitted (see Table 2). Therefore, it cannot be expected that improvement in drinking will be salient, and the increased drinking scores at follow-up must be evaluated in this light. Secondly, the scale contains both study and control cases, whereas it had been anticipated that the experimental treatment would show better results than the control treatment when compared in terms of the patients' social functioning level at follow-up. By separately analyzing the study and the control cases, this expected pattern is borne out. With respect to drinking intensity, the experimental patients did have a better outcome than the control cases.

TABLE 3.   Distribution of Follow-up Drinking Scale Scores

Scale Score	Frequency	Per Cent
0	3	3.0
1	9	9.0
2	5	5.0
3	11	11.0
4	30	30.0
5	42	42.0
TOTAL	100	100.0

The validity of the follow-up scale itself also improved when the two types of cases were handled separately. The coefficient for the over-all follow-up scale containing both study and control cases was 0.90. For study cases only, the coefficient increased to 0.91, and for the controls, 0.94.

Comparison of Drinking Levels Before and After Treatment

The predominate pattern for both the study and the control cases is one of increased drinking during the follow-up period, but this increase was more pronounced for the control than for the study group. At admission, the study cases had a median drinking score of 3.1, which at follow-up had increased to 4.0. By comparison, the control cases had a median drinking score of 3.3 at admission, which had risen to 4.6 at follow-up. Thus, the control patients had increased their drinking to a greater extent than the study patients, the difference in the scale scores being 1.3 and 0.9, respectively.

As seen in Table 4, more than one out of every four study patients (28.4 percent) showed improved drinking patterns after treatment, but this was the pattern demonstrated by less than one-half this proportion (12.1 percent) of the control group. Roughly the same proportions of both types of patients stayed at the same levels of drinking during the test period, that is, about 14 percent.

Again, the differences between the treatment approaches are expressed by the differences of patients whose drinking scores increased between admission and follow-up. Approximately three out of every four control patients (72.7 percent) had increased their drinking score, compared with three out of every five study cases (58.2 percent).

The significance of these differences between study and control patients with regard to the changes in their drinking patterns before and after treatment is attested to by the chi square value of 3.17, significant between the probability levels of 0.10 and 0.05.

Level of Drinking and Chances of Improvement

The evidence suggested by this analysis is that the less heavy drinkers at admission had a somewhat better chance

TABLE 4. Comparison of Drinking Scale Scores of Study and Control Cases Before and After Treatment

Treatment Received	Comparison of Scale Scores at Admission and Follow-Up:						Total	
	Lower Score at Follow-Up		Same Score at Follow-Up		Higher Score at Follow-Up			
	No.	%	No.	%	No.	%	No.	%
Study	19	28.4	9	13.4	39	58.2	67	100.0
Control	4	12.1	5	15.2	24	72.7	33	100.0
TOTAL	23	23.0	14	14.0	63	63.0	100	100.0

for improving than the heaviest drinkers. Thus, the higher the score at admission to the program, the higher the score would be at follow-up. The rank order correlation between the two scales showed that although the degree of relationship was quite low, the direction of the association between the scores was in a positive direction and the coefficient was slightly higher for the study than for the control cases, 0.099 and 0.045 respectively.[13]

Since these relationships were of a low order, the data were analyzed in another way to see if a more discernible pattern would emerge. Again the findings were only suggestive, but the direct relationship was maintained between the level of drinking at admission to the program and at follow-up (see Table 6). Of the study cases with a low score (three or less) at admission, 39 percent also had a low score at follow-up.

TABLE 5.   Matrix of Drinking Scale Scores
Before and After Treatment, Study Cases Only

Follow-Up Scores	In-Take Drinking Scores						
	0	1	2	3	4	5	Total
0	0	0	0	2	0	0	2
1	0	0	3	5	1	0	9
2	0	0	1	1	3	0	5
3	0	2	1	3	0	1	7
4	0	0	4	11	4	3	22
5	0	1	4	8	8	1	22
TOTAL	0	3	13	30	16	5	67

TABLE 6.   Comparison of Drinking Levels Before and After Treatment, Study Cases Only

Follow-Up Drinking Score	In-Take Drinking Scores					
	Low Score		High Score		Total	
	No.	%	No.	%	No.	%
Low	18	39.1	5	23.8	23	35.3
High	28	60.9	16	76.2	44	67.7
TOTAL	46	100.0	21	100.0	67	100.0

However, of the study cases with a high score (four or five) at admission, only 24 percent had a low score at follow-up. Although there is considerable likelihood that these differences are due to chance fluctuations (chi square value of 1.49, $P = 0.3$ and 0.2), the pattern supports the expected relationship.

Excerpts from the case summaries below depict the changes that are concisely measured by the scale scores. The first case is a patient who had a lower scale score at follow-up than he had at admission, indicating the type of improvement he experienced in his drinking levels between the two interviews.

Score change from five to three: The respondent's drinking pattern is stable in style and diminishing in quantity. He does not drink to intoxication, has not had blackouts, DT's, or other symptoms commonly seen in alcoholics. He came to the treatment unit because he felt he could not stop drinking by himself. At the time of admission, he was drinking three and one-half pints of whiskey in a 24-hour period. At the time of follow-up, he is consuming this amount, but over a period of a week rather than daily. He drinks every day, but he feels he can now control his drinking, and he has not been drunk since leaving the Unit.

The respondent's employment history has been one of manual labor, and his work record is not impressive. He has been on his present job for three months. He has lost perhaps a week of work when he would "have the blues" and decide not to go in to work for a day. During the past year he has had three jobs counting his present one. There is no change in his work pattern from the time of admission to follow-up; it is standard for him.

The next illustration is a case who stopped drinking after treatment and maintained this pattern for the entire follow-up period. Although this person needed additional help during the follow-up period, he never required in-patient hospital care. His job changes during the test period indicated the search for satisfying work, rather than the search for new jobs because he was fired or left work as a consequence of drinking.

Score change from three to one: The patient was very happy and cheerful throughout the interview as he was celebrating his first year of complete sobriety. During the follow-up period he has had numerous contacts with psychiatry, medicine, and social work on an out-patient basis. There have been no periods of hospitalization for any reason. The respondent characterizes his health as excellent and has had no health difficulties in the past year. He freely admits to being an alcoholic and to attending AA meetings more than once a week.

At the present time, the respondent is residing in a half-way house for alcoholics. He enjoys his living arrangements and has no intention of moving at the present time. He is an active church-goer. He has not been arrested for any violations during the past year.

The respondent was not employed immediately after discharge from the Unit. The first job he did find was with a wholesale company as a salesman working 48 hours and making $80 a week. He terminated this employment voluntarily as he did not care for the type of work. He did however return to this company for a short period of time when he was unable to find other work. Later he got a temporary job as a waiter and worked at this for several months. Eventually he became an attendant at a hospital where he is still employed, and makes about one-half the money that he did on his previous jobs, but is much happier in this type of work.

The following is an example of a person whose drinking became worse during the follow-up period.

Scale score change from four to five: My first impression of the patient was that physically he did not look as if he had changed a great deal from the time of his original interview. In terms of his employment and drinking patterns, however, these have both deteriorated during the past months following his discharge.

The patient is very vague about employment and says that when he does work he will do casual daily work out of the labor pool. He said that for the past year he has been doing more drinking than working, and that he would drink and use up the money and then when he could not get anything to drink from anybody, he would sober up and go back to work for a few days until he was able to earn enough money to start drinking again.

These case summaries illustrate in a descriptive manner positive change and negative change among the participants in the study as indexed by the comparison of drinking scale scores at admission to the treatment program and at one year or more following their discharge.

SUMMARY AND CONCLUSIONS

The aim of this work is to apply systematic and objective methods to measuring the eventual adjustment levels of persons who have received different kinds of treatment for alcoholism. Much of the previous research on this subject is inadequate because arbitrary and subjective methods have been used in the evaluation process, and as a consequence of the methodological deficiencies, either inconclusive or inconsistent results have been reported.

In this study, rigorous and objective measures have been used instead of unspecified and often illusive criteria that characterize many of the other attempts to assess treatment outcome. Through Guttman scaling techniques, a drinking scale was developed in which five items were identified, scored, and applied to the drinking patterns of persons who had participated in two different alcoholism treatment programs. Thus, the level of drinking of the participants could be compared before and after treatment, and the members of the two different treatment groups could be evaluated along the same dimensions.

This analysis showed that the great majority of these working-class persons admitted to the hospital treatment facility were well advanced in the progressive sequence of alcoholism. Not only was their drinking heavy, but it had reached the point where it interfered with carrying out work responsibilities.

On the whole, the persons in the study, regardless of the treatment received, increased their drinking during the year or more following their discharge from the program. This progressive deterioration, however, was more pronounced for the persons who had received the usual type of short-term hospital treatment for alcoholism than it was for the persons who had received the more extensive long-term care. Although few persons attained total abstinence for the entire follow-up period, the value of the experimental program was demonstrated by the proportions who managed to decrease their drinking. Proportionately twice as many of the experimental as the control cases decreased their drinking scores following treatment. Further indication of the value of the experimental program is the fact that the increase in drinking level was greater for the control than for the experimental group.

The evidence is clear that there is little likelihood for the alcoholic to stay at the same level of drinking for as long as a period of a year. Drinking will either increase, or it will decrease, but it will not stay the same.

The findings from this research indicate that the current organization of services established for treating alcoholism is quite costly. The time, money, and efforts that are now put into the limited care administered to alcoholics is insufficient, for little progress can be expected from the short-term, physically-oriented approach toward the treatment of alcoholism which is the all-too-frequent practice in hospitals. The kind of program necessary for adequately treating alcoholism must be conceived of in terms of longer and more extensive help with social and personal problems, and does not cease with the person's release from the hospital setting. Although such service may be more expensive than that ordinarily provided, it is not so when measured in terms of the long-range consequences.

Earlier detection and treatment programs are also needed so that intervention into the progressive deteriorating effects of alcoholism can be made at a time when treatment can have more impact. Given the state of current knowledge, by the time that many individuals obtain help, it is too late to make much alteration in their life patterns. Integration into the reward system of the larger society is essential, and participation in the labor force is one crucial aspect of this. The persons included in this study, and representative of populations served by public institutions in general, were, on the whole, at semi- or unskilled occupational levels. Because of their lack of skill, such persons in their adult years are, at best, tenuous in the labor force. When this fact is coupled with their alcoholism, the prospects are limited for improving their over-all social functioning. Such help must be provided at an earlier stage in their careers.

When expectations regarding the cure of alcoholism are not met because the impact of the illness has advanced beyond a point of change, and with the inadequate treatment rendered to alcoholics, the perspective that alcoholics cannot be helped is developed and supported. To change this attitude, treatment possibilities must be explored, improved, and expanded.

PART VI

Social Responses
to Alcoholism

14

Analysis of
Various Community Approaches
to the Problem of Alcoholism
in the United States

DAVID J. PITTMAN, MURIEL W. STERNE

The prevalence of alcoholism in America makes this one of the community's major social problems. Gross estimates indicate that of the approximately 80 million users of alcoholic beverages in America over 6 million are excessive users and may be classified as alcoholics. Thus, in frequency of occurrence alcoholism stands fourth in health problems in the United States, outranked only by mental illnesses, heart diseases, and cancer.

But, an equally salient fact is that the expansion of treatment facilities has lagged far behind the growth of the drinking problem, and it is only recently that federal officials have shown an interest in this problem, although state and local interest is of longer duration.

Although certain communities, such as Rochester, New York, to name only one, have better than average organizations for combatting alcoholism, American communities fail to deal effectively with all the dimensions of the alcoholism problem. By looking only at the present disparity between the magnitude of the problem and the relative paucity of

THIS chapter is adapted from David J. Pittman and Muriel W. Sterne, *The Carousel: Hospitals, Social Agencies, and the Alcoholic,* Report presented to the Missouri Division of Health, 1962.

treatment facilities, it is a simple task to criticize both public officials and health and welfare personnel for their lack of initiative. But, in making such criticisms, it is similarly easy to discount the important question of why there have been resistances to providing assistance for alcoholics. These resistances, centering not only in the lay population but also in professional groups of physicians, social workers, and nurses, are residuals of historical moralistic orientations, as well as being based on indifference and misinformation.

AMERICAN COMMUNITY ORGANIZATION AND ALCOHOLISM

Current approaches in American communities toward alcoholism and problem drinking are rooted in community attitudes toward drinking and the excessive drinkers. These attitudes are best understood within the historical framework of how alcoholism has been usually perceived and the means by which attitudinal changes toward alcoholism and innovation in the alcoholic's care have occurred.

National interest in the drinking problem, however, is not a new phenomenon. The Temperance Movement, which reached its zenith with the ratification of the Eighteenth Amendment in 1920, has a history which encompasses more than a century. But all major Prohibitionist groups, historical or contemporary, have a strongly moralistic tenor, and the goals of these groups reflect a variety of religious and reformist aspirations.

It was not until the 1930s that a large-scale movement with a treatment orientation toward alcoholism first took shape with the appearance of Alcoholics Anonymous in 1934 and the establishment of an American Research Council on Alcoholism four years later. In 1940 the first issue of the *Quarterly Journal of Studies on Alcohol*, a scientific journal dealing with such problems as the physiological, psychosocial, and cultural ramifications of alcohol and alcohol usage was published at the Laboratory of Applied Biodynamics, Yale University, by the Journal of Studies on Alcohol, Inc. In 1943 the Yale Sum-

mer School of Alcohol Studies was established to give training
to interested personnel in this field, and in 1945 the National
Council on Alcoholism was organized to disseminate information to the general public. This new approach focussed on
removing the stigma from alcoholism and, in the case of the
Yale School and the Research Council on Alcoholism, making
it the object of scientific investigation and assistance. Whereas
in the past the state and local governments had conceived
their roles as controlling the sale of alcohol and punishing
the alcoholic offender, the new emphasis viewed alcoholism
as a problem of public health. In accordance with this out-
look, Oregon, in 1943, initiated the first state public health
program aimed at alcoholism.[1] By 1966, 42 states had official
agencies on alcoholism.

It would be a mistake, however, to imply that the public
health approach to alcoholism was widespread and always
accepted with little or no resistance. Although the repeal of
Prohibition in 1933 was a serious blow for the old moralistic
view of alcoholism, attitudes which had predominated for
better than a century were not easily discarded, and those
who proposed the adoption of the public health approach
often met with strong opposition from vested interest groups.
For example, individuals, such as the Prohibitionists, with
strong emotional investment in their cause, were and still are
hesitant to lay aside their fervent dedication in order to make
way for an antithetical approach. Furthermore, the resistance
of the beverage industry to a public health approach in many
states has resulted in failure to create effective programs to
deal with alcoholism because of a lack of funds on the state
or local level. Thus, the alcohol industry in many areas has,
perhaps unwittingly, reinforced the Prohibitionistic philosophy
that the alcoholic is responsible for his condition. Furthermore, the simple fact that people are not eager to disturb
the *status quo* also obstructs the implementation of new ideas.

Creating and maintaining effective state programs for alcoholism are made doubly complex by the conflict between the
"wet" and "dry" sentiments coexisting in many communities.
Among the former are religious groups whose ceremonies
include the use of alcohol (e.g., the Jews), persons who have

traditionally regarded the use of liquor as the appropriate means of expressing hospitality and sociability (e.g., Irish-Catholics), and, of course, the liquor industry. The "drys" are characteristically composed of ascetic Protestant groups who believe that the use of alcohol is sinful and who therefore see little difference between the occasional social drinker and the chronic inebriate, for the former is the prodromal stage for the latter. The impediment which arises in trying to develop a state program for alcohol education is that any attempt to teach the intelligent use of alcohol in moderate amounts would violate the cultural norms and values of abstinent groups, while advocating total abstinence would evoke a negative reaction from the "wets" for the same reason. The end result of such a conflict has been that even where provision is made for education on alcohol and alcoholism, local authorities have been reluctant to carry out such a program. Even in those communities which have an alcoholism education program in the schools, emphasis is placed on the more neutral area of the physiological effects of alcohol and/or the delivery of inspirational talks by Alcoholics Anonymous members. A recent report on such programs noted that:

Up to 1943, practically every state had laws requiring public school instruction on alcoholism but educators were understandably cautious in their meeting statutory requirements . . . Feelings and attitudes from former experiences and controversies kept alive and aggravated strong differences of opinions about goals, methods, and subject matter (Note 1, p. 139).

Resistance to the treatment of the alcoholic is found in the slow recognition by professional health and social welfare personnel (physicians, psychiatrists, and social workers, for example) that alcoholism is a disease requiring their special knowledge and skills. It was not until 1956 that the American Medical Association expressed the opinion that alcoholism should come under the scope of medical practice, that hospitals should make provisions for the care of alcoholics, and that medical interns should be trained in the treatment of alcoholics. The next year, 1957, the *Journal of the American Medical Association* finally gave its official approval to the statement that alcoholism is a disease. The same year, the

American Hospital Association followed by urging that each case of alcoholism be examined individually to determine whether or not the condition was amenable to medical treatment. Both of these positions represented a notable change from the practices reported in a 1944 study of the American Hospital Association, in which "treatment for the alcoholic was viewed with considerable skepticism." (Note 1, p. 141). To some extent, the helping professions have assumed that certain victims of the disease who have formed themselves into "Alcoholics Anonymous" groups were the only ones to have any significant impact on alcoholism. This position, while having truth for some alcoholics, results in medicine, psychiatry, and social work abdicating their responsibility for the professional care of the alcoholic.

Even when there is consensus among individuals that alcoholism is a major health problem and should be treated, there is still a frustrating area of disagreement as to the precise nature of the ailment and the specific type of care which should be given. Some psychiatric personnel consider alcoholism to be symptomatic of an underlying psychic disorder and hence, place no emphasis on the manifest drinking problem. Others consider the debilitating effects of alcoholism and the accompanying social maladjustment as the main obstacles to recovery and therefore focus on arresting the pattern of inebriety. Another point of discord concerns the type and arrangement of facilities for use in the treatment process—whether alcoholics should be treated in general, medical, psychiatric, or special alcoholic facilities; whether they should be segregated from or dispersed among patients with other diagnoses. These professional disagreements, while having the common virtue of assuming that the alcoholic needs care, have tended to hamper efforts to establish a common cooperative approach to alcoholism.

All of the above controversies, irrespective of the orientation from which they arise, compound the problem of few resources with which to meet a widespread need. Our culture, with its ethos of individual responsibility and free choice, has not emphasized subsidizing health and welfare programs, and even with a concerted effort to obtain maximum efficiency from the limited facilities, there is likely to be a disparity between the extent of the problem and the efforts made to counteract it. Therefore, any conflict which decreases the utilization of these resources complicates an already difficult situation.

THE POSITION OF THE ALCOHOLISM PROBLEM IN AMERICAN COMMUNITIES

In planning a total community organization effort for combatting alcoholism, there are a number of problems of which community members should be aware. These problems exist in varying degrees in all American communities. They are:

1. *There is an extensive and increasing alcoholism problem in American communities.* Computations using the unrevised Jellinek Estimation Formula indicate that there have been significant increases in the number of alcoholics from 1940 to 1966 in most American communities.

2. *There is an absence of clearly defined responsibility, both academically and clinically, for alcoholism.* Academically, since the emergence of the scientific, public health, and disease orientations toward alcoholism, most researchers and a significant portion of clinicians have assumed that alcoholism is most amenable to study from an interdisciplinary point of view.

The interdisciplinary research orientation posits the comprehension of alcoholism within the context of biological, psychological, cultural, sociological, and pharmacological studies; rarely is there any attempt to integrate the approach of two or more disciplines in a single study. This research approach is assumed because there is an absence of any precise and uniform definition of alcoholism and the shrouding in mystery of alcoholism etiology. This orientation, however, is quite in keeping with scientific procedures for the study of such an elusive problem as alcoholism. This interdisciplinary position has limitations for the treatment personnel who must cope with the clinical problem of alcoholism. This is reflected in the fact that many clinicians are perplexed and confused concerning who is an alcoholic, what the etiology of alcoholism is, whether the problem is a disease or indicative of moral weakness, and how to appropriately treat the alcoholic. Furthermore, treatment personnel even with a disease orientation show pessimism toward the treatability of the alcoholic.

But the major problem is the lack of a locus of responsibility for the treatment and long-term care of the alcoholic in a community. This has led to the negative situation of a merry-go-round of referrals for the alcoholic. Data from various communities indicate that agencies without intensive casework see this service as essential; casework agencies, however, perceive alcoholism as involving a psychiatric component and referral to psychiatric facilities as indispensable; but the psychiatric facilities have few alcoholics in treatment and frequently refer them to the lay organization, Alcoholics Anonymous. In some cases alcoholic patients and/or clients are referred to services which either do not accept them or are not particularly anxious to work with them. Furthermore, A.A.'s emphasis on the alcoholic's initiating contact with it seems to have been generalized by treatment agents to other referral resources, despite the fact that research has shown that referral by direction is much less effective than referral in which the treatment agent initiates contact for the patient or client with the agency to which he is referring. Thus, the referral system has a tendency to break down and leaves the impression, partially unwarranted, that the alcoholic will not accept referrals to other agencies.

3. *The alcoholic patient and/or client occupies an ambiguous role.* The dilemma which confronts treatment personnel is, to what extent is the alcoholic a unique patient requiring special facilities and techniques of treatment? In certain general hospitals and social agencies the rationalization for failure to accept alcoholics for treatment is built on the assumed necessity for special facilities and orientations. To a certain extent this position is justifiable if viewed in historical perspective. Traditionally, professional training in nursing, medicine, and social work, to mention three, have ignored the alcoholic. It is not unusual for one trained in the above-mentioned professions to have had only minimal contact with this problem.

This lack of experience plus negative attitudes have made certain general hospitals and agencies skeptical as to whether the alcoholic is a part of their responsibility, leading to the movements for establishment of special facilities (which from our experience is an essential part of any community's program for alcoholism).

4. *There is a significant core of negative sentiment toward the alcoholic on the part of the community hospital and agency personnel.* Many treatment personnel are marked by ambivalence, moralism, and pessimism regarding the alcoholic and his treatability. Our research studies show a significant relationship between the perception of alcoholics as presenting problems for treatment and the respondents' unwillingness to accept them as patients. Those treatment personnel viewing alcoholics as problem patients are most likely to state that they do not have the facilities to treat these patients. Furthermore, personnel who scored high in moralism tended to be more pessimistic than did those who scored low in moralism. Also, those personnel who are pessimistic about the treatment of alcoholism rate the alcoholic more negatively in terms of his role performance as a client or a patient. These attitudes of pessimism and defeatism are automatically registered into any treatment situation which, of course, has negative implications for the therapist-patient relationship.

Members of the medical profession were more willing than those in social work to perceive the negative attitudes of treatment personnel toward the alcoholic as being a major factor in the pessimistic orientation toward the prognosis of the disease. But the situation is not one of pervasive negativism on the part of these personnel. There are many who are aware that they are dealing with a chronic disease of long duration for which there are no readily available cures.

Unfortunately, many treatment personnel have reified the motivation concept to the point that it describes and judges alcoholics instead of explaining their behavior. There is a danger that the term "patient motivation" may be only a more sophisticated version of the scientifically discarded willpower concept.

5. *There is the absence of well-defined community agency*

leadership in coping with the alcoholism problem. Much discussion in American communities has centered around the merits of the specialized versus the generalized approach to alcoholism. In the generalized approach, all concerned agencies and hospitals accept and work with the alcoholic much in the same sense that general hospitals admit pneumonia patients and social agencies see people with family problems. Perhaps this is ideally the case if treatment personnel operate on the assumption that the alcoholic is another chronically ill person. *But this is not the case in American communities!*

There must be a central source of disseminating knowledge and information concerning the treatment of the alcoholic and an agency which is perceived as providing accurate and up-to-date information about the problem. Experience indicates that a local council on alcoholism with an information center best meets these needs.

GUIDELINES FOR COMMUNITY ALCOHOLISM PROGRAMS

In developing community alcoholism programs certain guidelines for consideration in planning should be noted. These are:

1. *State Responsibility.* Given the extensiveness of the alcoholism problem in the nation and in any state, the federal and state governments must assume part of the responsibility for the activities of education, prevention, treatment, and research in the area of alcoholism. The mechanism for this aim on the state level, whether through a state commission on alcoholism, within existing state agencies of health, mental health, or chronic disease control, is best left to those having an intimate knowledge of the state situation. On the federal level, in 1966, there is no central locus of responsibility for alcoholism control; this is one major reason for the current deficiencies in federal alcoholism activities.

2. *Local Responsibility.* The problem of combatting alcoholism, however, is one that involves responsibility on the part of health and welfare agencies on the local community

level. On the whole these efforts have been fragmentary and
deficient in reference to alcoholism control.

3. *Hospital Facilities.* Better in- and out-patient care facilities for the alcoholic are indicated. Clinical experience has
shown that a large section of the alcoholic population in the
acute stages can be treated with minimal difficulty within
the context of the general hospital. Therefore, general hospitals should place into operation the recommendation of the
American Hospital Association, i.e., that they provide care
for the alcoholic under a primary diagnosis of alcoholism.
Given the fact that there are negative orientations toward
general hospital care of the alcoholic, it will perhaps be
necessary for some years to have specialized or segregated
facilities for the care of the alcoholic. Hospitals can make
a strong contribution to better understanding of the alcoholic
if the subterfuge of secondary diagnosis is abandoned. This
problem would perhaps be alleviated by the removal of
restrictive hospital insurance provisions concerning the alcoholic.

4. *Social Agencies.* The social agencies should increase their
concern and their services for the alcoholic client. Agencies
and in-treatment facilities for the alcoholic need to coordinate
their services in order to bridge the treatment gap between
the hospital and the community. Agencies frequently report
alcoholics do not seek their services, while hospitals generally
lack an effective out-patient treatment procedure for alcoholics.

To cope with the fact that alcoholics are reluctant to keep
their appointments or to continue with an agency once they
have started, agencies should re-examine their techniques of
working with alcoholics. A technique of positive aggressive-
ness in which agency workers take the initiative in continuing
relationships with the patient is indicated.

Also, agencies should re-examine their positions in reference
to how essential patient motivation is for treatment. There is
the danger that motivation may be used as a scientifically
accepted term for the discredited will power concept.

As is also the case for medical and nursing personnel, social
agencies need to re-examine the attitudes of their personnel

toward the alcoholic in order to reduce the negative and pessimistic beliefs present.

5. *The Chronic Drunkenness Offender.* The most difficult group of alcoholics in terms of treatment and rehabilitation is that hard core, chiefly men, who are involved in a "revolving door" process of intoxication, arrest, incarceration, release, reintoxication, and rearrest. The police, the courts, and the penal institutions need to re-examine and to coordinate their policies of coping with this group of chronic offenders. Leads for handling the chronic intoxication case can be obtained from studying existent programs in Seattle, Los Angeles, Boston, and Rochester, New York. The agencies mentioned above should investigate the possibility of jointly establishing long-term treatment facilities such as domiciliaries and half-way houses for these offenders. Such programs will require revision of state statutes and/or local ordinances concerning the chronic drunkenness offender, especially in light of court decisions in the Driver and Easter cases (Chapter 9).

15

Alcoholics Anonymous: An Interpretation

MILTON A. MAXWELL

It is probable that more contemporary alcoholics have found sobriety through the fellowship of Alcoholics Anonymous than through all other agencies combined. Yet the "A.A. recovery program" remains an unknown quantity to many, and at least

REPRINTED with permission of John Wiley & Sons, Inc., *Society, Culture, and Drinking Patterns,* edited by David J. Pittman and Charles R. Snyder, New York, 1962.

something of an enigma to most. It is agreed that, for many alcoholics, the A.A. program "works," but what makes it work? What are the therapeutic dynamics? At this point, even social scientists and clinicians close to the alcoholism problem are often baffled. They find it difficult to reconcile what they know or think they know about A.A. with their theoretical assumptions about the nature of alcoholism on the one hand and the imperatives of the therapeutic processes on the other. The interpretation that follows—limited and incomplete as it must be—is based on the assumption that enigmatic qualities of A.A. are more apparent than real, and that the A.A. program "makes sense" in the light of contemporary social science concepts and assumptions.

CONDITIONS FOR CHANGE

How then, we may ask, can the alcoholic change? If the more he uses alcohol as his means of relief the worse he gets, and if he is unable to control its consumption, how can he escape his dilemma? Paradoxically, the answer seems to be that he cannot escape his predicament until he faces the fact that by himself he cannot escape it. It appears, further-more, that the alcoholic has to become completely disillu-sioned, not only with his own ability to solve his alcohol problem, but also with alcohol as his method of solving any problems. This includes the conviction that his drinking which for years was considered to be an asset has definitely become a liability and, if continued, will lead only to more suffering, degradation, and perhaps insanity, or even death. For the dis-illusionment with alcohol to be complete, however, it appar-ently must include the conviction that any compromise goal of safe, controlled drinking is utterly impossible for him. The average alcoholic knows what the ultimate outcome of com-pulsive drinking is, but he finds it difficult to believe that this fate is in store for him until he is completely convinced that he is an "uncontrolled drinker."

Such disillusionment was reported in a study of 150 A.A. members.[1] Asked what had happened just before joining A.A.

to make them ready for A.A., some of the respondents simply expressed their over-all feeling of despair. For example, the comments ran as follows: (a) "Complete feeling of being 'licked.' Dejected and remorseful—'down and out' "; (b) "The feeling [that] I was just in a sort of whirl-pool which was slowly taking me beyond hope"; (c) "A beaten, hopeless person, my back to the wall"; and (d) "At the end of the rope."

About 25 per cent replied in terms similar to these, obviously implying their inability to control their drinking, but another 35 per cent specifically listed the conviction of being an uncontrolled drinker as the factor which made them ready for A.A. help. For example, one respondent stated: "I finally faced the obvious fact that my drinking was completely out of control. I'd tried many so-called systems to limit my drinking and failed." Still another 28 per cent mentioned some jolting event which gave a disillusioning, crisis definition to their use of alcohol. Most often listed was the loss or threatened loss of job or spouse. Also listed were such events as arrest for drunken driving, hospitalization or illness because of drinking, fractured skull in a fall while drunk, rejection of a life insurance application, insane behavior during a drinking bout, blackouts, and hallucinations.

Apparently, however, disillusionment is only one of the major prerequisites for readiness to seek help. A certain number, obviously implying their disillusionment with their alcoholic way of life, reported the discovery that there was a way out as the factor which made them ready for A.A. This is the prerequisite of "hope," without which an active movement toward help is not conceivable.

In the case of these particular subjects, the hope was usually introduced by a recovered alcoholic—an A.A. member. And here we can pinpoint one of A.A.'s great strengths. The mere information that A.A. (or any therapeutic program) can work introduces hope into an alcoholic's situation. How much more convincing, then, is the flesh-and-blood example of a person for whom the program has worked! In addition, if this same "recovered" alcoholic, through his accepting and understanding attitude, can also help the prospect face and accept an honest, disillusioning appraisal of his drinking problem, it is much easier to bring about the particular intersection of disillusionment and hope which constitutes "readiness" to move toward help.

Such a meaningful coming together of disillusionment and hope seems to be a very individual matter. It may occur early as in the case of what A.A.'s call "high bottoms." It may not occur until after many years of suffering ("low bottoms"), and it may not occur at all, but there is nothing fateful about it. More early-stage and early-middle-stage alcoholics are affiliating with A.A. and are being seen in the growing number of alcoholic clinics as a result of alcoholism education and the therapeutic success of A.A. and other programs.

Whether disillusionment and hope intersect early or late, it appears that both are prerequisites for readiness to seek or accept help. It follows, accordingly, that these prerequisites should be the first two steps in the A.A. program of recovery:

1. We admitted we were powerless over alcohol—that our lives had become unmanageable.
2. Came to believe that a Power greater than ourselves could restore us to sanity.

THE GREATER POWER CONCEPT

The naturalistically oriented reader who has been following this analysis without difficulty up to this point finds himself up against language which may block his understanding of A.A. at a crucial point. What is he to make of William James' phrase, "a Power greater than ourselves," especially if this is then equated with "God as we understood Him"? It may therefore be appropriate to point out that a naturalistic interpretation of the "Greater Power" concept is possible.

The reader can, for example, recognize the fact that there are powers—resources of many kinds—to help an alcoholic recover. He can also recognize the fact that these resources for recovery are quite beyond the isolated, alibi-ridden, and anxious alcoholic. If one is sophisticated in the use of the concept of "self," one can recognize that these resources believed to be within the individual are nevertheless beyond and outside the "self" as the alcoholic knows himself. These resources are not effectively but only potentially present.

Moreover, it can be accepted that the potential resources are empirically identifiable resources. They consist of real energies locked up or wasted in conflict, burned up in anxiety and depleted through neglect of health. They consist of blocked and unused mental powers. They consist of the potential capacities to be "productive" in Erich Fromm's sense of being able to love, to give, and to accomplish. All these and other potential resources are "there"—they are "real."

As far as the alcoholic is concerned, however, they are anything but "there." It is even difficult for him to believe that they are potentially present. Yet, to move out of his dilemma, he has to develop some belief, tentative and partial though it may be, that the potential resources are real—are available to him—and are capable of restoring him to normalcy. This is the hope of step two.

Next the alcoholic is asked to turn himself over to this potential—to abandon his constricted and hopeless position and to "surrender" or "give in" to the "life forces" potentially available. This would be the naturalistic interpretation of the third step:

3. Made a decision to turn our will and lives over to the care of God *as we understood Him.*

It might be added that, in actual practice, atheists, agnostics, naturalists, and a great variety of supernaturalists have found it possible to take this important step thanks largely to the phrase *"as we understood Him,"* and to the general practice of requiring nothing more than some concept of some power or powers other than what the particular alcoholic is able to command at the time. This may be the group. It may be the program. It may be a liberal or orthodox concept of God. It may be anything which meaningfully symbolizes to the individual the potential resources on which to base his hope of recovery.

Thus, the first three steps in the A.A. program are seen to consist of the necessary admission of powerlessness over alcohol and a hopeful willingness to let the more productive forces in the individual and his situation prevail. To the degree that the three prerequisites are met, the formerly impossible begins to happen. The log jam is broken. The emotional constriction is relaxed. The release of potential resources begins. Satisfying interactions with other persons again become possible. In short, the movement toward health begins.

THE TWELVE-STEP PROGRAM

Many of the elements of the Twelve-Step Program are seen in sharper relief in the original formulation of the steps by which Bill, A.A.'s cofounder, achieved sobriety. These are: you admit you are licked; you get honest with yourself; you talk it out with somebody else; you make restitution to the people you have harmed; you try to give of yourself without stint, with no demands for reward; and you pray to whatever God you think there is, even as an experiment, to help you to do these things.[2]

In this series of steps will be seen the admission of "powerlessness over alcohol" already discussed. Also implicit is the hope of a way out—faith in potential resources and complete reliance upon these resources. The other steps constitute quite an additional order: honest self-analysis and catharsis; the mending of social fences; the practice of out-going, giving, productive behavior for its own sake and not for ego-defense or reassurance; and, finally, the cultivation of the "potential resources" as understood by the individual. Much could be written about the therapeutic value of these steps, for there is wide consensus about the importance of an honest facing of oneself and the unburdening of guilts, fears, and repressed material in the presence of an accepting person, and about the importance of cultivating the desired attitudes and practicing the desired patterns of behavior. However, the Twelve Steps do not exhaust the A.A. program. The interpersonal and group aspects of the A.A. fellowship also play a very important therapeutic role.

THE PERSONALITY CHANGES

That personality changes occur in A.A. is accepted. It is true that the degree or range of change varies greatly from person to person. Some merely achieve sobriety without any other observable change. Yet, in perspective, even this achievement is a dramatic one. In the writer's opinion, however, the majority exhibit additional and sometimes very substantial changes in personality.

The changes and direction of change may be seen in the case material upon which the writer has previously reported.[3] The following seven replies are representative of the kinds of "attitudes, desires, fears, etc." which A.A. had helped its members to "give up" to some degree:

a. I gave up intolerance, jealousy, self-pity, anger as much as possible, desire for power and a lot of money, being critical.

b. Self-pride, conceit, headstrong attitude, fears of others and their opinion of me, fear of my thoughts, fear of inadequacy and fear of insecurity.

c. The attitudes of egotism, vanity, selfishness, etc., and the desire of wanting to be a big shot—the big I (without of course trying to even deserve such a title).

d. Have tried to give up selfishness, "Big I" attitude, running others my way, desire for money as such, false social position, procrastination, fear of what people might say.

e. Gave up the fear of loving anyone wholeheartedly, even my child; fear of life for myself and others; thinking it smart to be caustic and overbearing.

f. Am relinquishing the attitude of self-importance and the feeling of the need to emphasize my qualifications compared to those of others . . .

g. Gave up formless fears, fear of failure, sense of inadequacy, fear of people or love . . . and pretense of being other than one of the "little people" who are bound by the limitations of their own undeveloped potentialities.

More systematically summarized, the list of reported changes was led on the one hand by the reduction of interpersonal anxieties, ego-inflation, hostility, and intolerance, and, in a listing of values gained, by an increase in the ability to interact more satisfyingly with other persons. Reportedly gained was the greater enjoyment and appreciation not only of other persons but also of other facets of life; a greater ability to face and accept reality; greater objectivity with regard to self—honesty, humility, and sense of humor and of proportion; an increase in the sense of security, adequacy, confidence, worth, and accomplishment; physical and emotional relaxation; and, finally—and frequently listed—"peace of mind."

If any one trend stands out in these reported changes, it is the modification of self-other attitudes and perceptions in the direction of what we have been calling a more productive orientation.

A complete accounting of personality changes is beyond the scope of present knowledge. We assume that such changes are the products of learning. We assume furthermore that the learning processes in A.A. are of the same kind found in any psychotherapy leading to the same changes. The language of psychotherapy could be used to describe and explain many aspects of the therapeutic dynamics to be found in A.A. (See for example Tiebout,[4-6] Stewart,[7, 8] Ripley and Jackson,[9] and Lindt.[10]) It is, however, possible and appropriate to conceive of the personality-changing dynamics in A.A. in more sociological concepts.

THE A.A. GROUP AND ITS SUBCULTURE

Kurt Lewin and Paul Grabbe[11] have provided us with a bridge in their suggestion that a change in personality may be conceptualized as a change in culture. Specifically, they suggested that to change is to accept a change in "facts" which are accepted as true, a change in values, and a change in the perception of self and others in a social field. To this we could add that the personality changes may also be seen as the acceptance of new norms—folkways and mores, new role-status system, a new charter, and new sanctions. These are all aspects of culture—of a group-shared way of life.

We may accordingly conceptualize the alcoholic's recovery in A.A. as the joining of a new group and, in that group, gradually learning that group's culture. The A.A. subculture, moreover, constitutes a way of life which is more realistic, which enables the member to get closer to people, which provides one with more emotional security, and which facilitates more productive living. Thus, the A.A. group becomes an important new reference group—a new point of orientation.

The A.A. group must also be seen as a primary group which provides exceptionally favorable learning conditions for the internalizing of this new way of life. Primary groups were so called by Cooley because they are more influential than other groups in shaping our attitudes. Among primary groups, however, some are more influential than others. The more intimate the group and the more totally involved its members become in each other and the group life, the greater is the influence of the group upon its members.

The writer's experience as a participant observer in an A.A. group for a summer impressed upon him the unusual quality of relationship to be found there—the intimacy, mutual acceptance, and identification. Unless these qualities of relationship are recognized and unless the "relearning potency" of such a group experience is appreciated, the observer will miss something very important about A.A.

To summarize the points just made: the A.A. group is to be understood as an unusually intimate primary group which sponsors, in a potent learning situation, a new way of life—a new subculture. Within this frame of reference, it is possible to analyze the content of this new learning and how it deals with the linkage of stress to alcohol drinking.

First, the A.A. subculture provides the member with much more objective knowledge about alcohol and particularly about alcoholism. This includes a redefinition of alcoholism as an illness rather than as moral degeneracy.

Second, the A.A. subculture requires and facilitates an honest facing of the connection between drinking and stressful situations; the alcoholic begins to define his disorder as involving an obsession of the mind. The impotency of will power to handle the obession and the necessity of other help are emphasized. Myths and rationalizations concerning drinking are debunked. The "screwy alcoholic thinking" is dissected and exposed, frequently in a humorous fashion.

Anxieties against drinking are buttressed. Alcohol is associated with all the harm it has done to the alcoholic and with the tragic increase rather than the solution of problems. The member is given perspective on the first drink—that he will always be just one drink from a drunk, and that he can never again drink socially. He is taught that he can "arrest" his problem but that he will always remain an alcoholic. This fact is reinforced each time he presides and introduces himself with "I'm Joe Doakes and I'm an alcoholic." Then, to handle the anxiety aroused by the dread of a lifetime without alcohol, he is provided with the "24-hour plan"—sobriety just one day at a time. Because of his association and identification with sobriety models, the A.A. system is made easier to accept and learn. Then when he steps out to help a new prospect (Twelfth-Step calls), he furthers his learning by becoming a teacher and a representative of the A.A. way of thinking and acting. Thus, the A.A. ideology not only attacks vigorously the use of alcohol for the relief of stress, it provides alternative methods of tension relief.

Important is the A.A. structuring of the freedom and the formal and informal opportunities to gain relief from tensions by the "talking-out" process. Important also are the club activities: the fellowship of the coffee bar, the bull sessions, the games, the parties, or the hours of private conversations over a cup of coffee somewhere. In countless ways, A.A. provides the rewards of satisfying social activities to replace the rewards previously sought in a drinking group, or simply sought in the bottle itself.

Outgoing activity in the form of "Twelfth-Step" work—working with other alcoholics—is another important mode of tension relief expected in A.A. In addition, the A.A. culture encourages the cultivation of hobbies, interests, and other means of tension relief. Included are meditation and prayer.

Not only does A.A. provide and encourage the learning (or relearning) of alternative relief methods, but the A.A. way of life also reduces the amount of stress for which relief is needed. When the compounding of stress through years of alcoholic drinking is considered, the reversal of the isolation, anxiety, and rationalization trends adds up to a substantial reduction of stress. In addition, acceptance of the A.A. way of life reduces the predrinking level of stress. This is done by providing the group member with values and norms and ways of perceiving his social world which are simply less anxiety-producing, which enable him to relate more satisfyingly to other people and, in general, to find more of the satisfactions of a productive orientation.

Other stress-reducing aspects of the A.A. way of life can be mentioned. There are the slogans repeated in the literature and usually posted in meeting places. "Live and let live" reminds the member of the importance of tolerance for others. "Keep an open mind" asks for tolerance of new ideas. "Easy does it" suggests relaxation in various tension-producing contexts. "But for the Grace of God" expresses thankfulness and reminds him of his dependence upon more than his own efforts. The value placed upon "honesty" and "humility" are a constant encouragement to a greater objectivity with regard to himself.

To be rated also are the low-pressure methods encouraged in A.A. This permissiveness has the function of reducing initial resistance. It constantly encourages respect for the rights of the other fellow—even his right to get drunk if he wants to.

Many other aspects of the A.A. way of life could be cited, but the above are sufficient to illustrate the present frame of reference through which the changes in the A.A. member's personality are seen as the learning of a new culture—a new way of life—in the favorable learning milieu of an exceptionally intimate primary group.

Lest too idealized an impression be left, however, it should be acknowledged that A.A. groups often fall short of providing an ideal learning environment. Even in the same group, the constellation of factors is less favorable for some members than for others.

In studying the favorable and unfavorable factors involved in affiliation with A.A., Trice[12, 13] found not only differences in attitude and knowledge on the part of those attempting to affiliate, but also differences in the receiving groups. Despite the injunctions of the program, prospects were not always provided with sponsorship. Nor were efforts always made to draw one into close relationships with the members.

The writer's own observations in many A.A. groups have led him to similar conclusions. Some groups are less energetic in reaching out to new members, less successful in sponsoring them and in overcoming their early fears. Some groups, furthermore, fail to provide as warm and intimate a climate as others. Thus they create group situations which are less favorable not only to affiliation but also to effective relearning.

It also appears that groups vary considerably in the psychological insight collectively possessed by their members—insight into the causes of alcoholism, the dynamics of personality, and even the personality-changing factors of the program and group activities of A.A. itself. Groups also vary in the maturity of the actual patterns of behavior prevailing in the group. This refers not only to the amount of rivalry, conflict, or other "immature" behavior, but also to the level of productive living which is espoused and to the seriousness with which this goal is pursued.

That these and other differences exist in A.A. groups should, of course, surprise no one, nor should the differences obscure the recognition that even the more ineffective groups, if they continue to exist at all, have achieved at last some success in learning and applying the A.A. way of life. Furthermore, the group differences should not obscure the appreciation that A.A. is an amazing phenomenon on the modern scene.

Not least remarkable is the fact that its program was worked out not by professional therapists but by a group of alcoholics themselves. A.A.'s success alone demonstrates that these laymen did indeed weave together a very effective pattern. Their lay language and spiritual concepts, however, have made it difficult for some social scientists and clinicians to appreciate fully the dynamics involved.[14]

16

Governmental Responses to Alcoholism in North America

AUGUSTUS H. HEWLETT

Repeal of Prohibition in the United States left a vast social vacuum concerning all problems dealing with beverage alcohol. Under the Volstead Act it had been against Federal law to produce, sell, consume, or possess alcoholic beverages for general consumption. All problems dealing with alcohol had been dealt with simply and legalistically; according to the mandate of the people in repealing Prohibition—erroneously. Suddenly, in 1933, the entire procedure for dealing with alcohol problems became obsolete.

Ernest Shepherd[1] has stated that Prohibition—which was the last great political thrust of the Temperance Movement—was defeated because of a negative response to it as a symbol as well as to its restrictions specifically. The rejection was of *any* controls of alcohol. This became so manifest as to become even a denial of *all* alcohol problems. It was a sweeping attitude. The public refused to recognize alcohol-related problems regardless of how obvious they might be. The public was most suspicious of anyone or any group which purported to work on any area of the alcohol problems. Thus, there is little wonder as to why Washington did not initiate early action to fill the vacuum born of repeal with constructive programs at the Federal level.

The modern day governmental interest in alcoholism problems in North America began during the middle of the 1940s at the state level, where there was more public tolerance of governmental involvement. Legislation was enacted in several states recognizing alcoholism as an illness and as a public health problem. By 1950 fourteen states in the United States and one Canadian province had enacted authorizing legislation for the establishment of alcoholism programs at the state/provincial level. Today, fifty-three programs at this level of government are in existence throughout the United States and Canada. These include eight provinces and the Yukon Territory in Canada; forty-two states, the District of Columbia and Puerto Rico.

These programs differ greatly in terms of their organizational structures, operational procedures, and scopes of activity. Their annual budgets range from less than $25,000 to several million dollars. Of the forty-four United States programs, ten are now organizationally independent units of government; twenty are located within Departments of Public Health; and fourteen are within Departments of Mental Health. The Canadian programs for the most part are independent governmental units with two exceptions—Saskatchewan places its alcoholism program within the Department of Social Welfare and Rehabilitation, and Alberta's program is a division of the Provincial Health Department.

Compared with other health and welfare programs, state alcoholism programs vary extensively. This is true because, for the most part, they came into being independently of one another with no national direction and with only a minimal amount of intercommunication. Compared, for instance, with the Vocational Rehabilitation programs, which have historically had national leadership, the state alcoholism movement grew without national planning. Whereas the Vocational Rehabilitation field has definite criteria, eligibility requirements, field-wide consensus on definitions, standards and procedures, there is no such uniformity within the alcoholism or alcohol problems field. In terms of objectives, goals, and philosophies, however, there is a great deal of uniformity within the ranks of governmental alcoholism programs.

All of these programs have, as their primary and in most cases their exclusive concern, the problems of alcoholism. Their ultimate goal could perhaps be stated generally as "The Eradication of Alcoholism." They would, again generally, divide their areas of concern into two broad categories.

(1) work on the existing alcoholic population; and (2) work towards the prevention of alcoholism.

Most of these programs support some type of treatment facilities—either inpatient or outpatient, and in some cases, both. All of them are involved to some degree in educational efforts and most of them have engaged or are now engaged in one or another kind of research activity.

Four principles have been employed historically by the governmental alcoholism programs.[1] The first is in the form of official policy restricting activities to alcoholism and the alcoholic, while maintaining strict neutrality or avoidance of the "wet-dry" issue. The second embraces the treatability of alcoholics concept—or the concept that the alcoholic can be treated effectively. The third is the principle of uniting various disciplines of many kinds of people in the community into a task force, which, as a team, can deal constructively with alcoholism as a many-sided condition. Fourth, is the principle of the use of tested knowledge. No single segment of the population nor any particular group is represented by an official agency, and the agency must be guided by tested knowledge in its formulation of public policy and action.

These were principles with which the official agencies began more than two decades ago, and they continue to prevail although some agencies are now beginning to look at alcohol-related problems other than those dealing exclusively with alcoholism.

Twenty years ago when only a few state programs had been established, public suspicion concerning governmental involvement in alcohol problems was very strong. Embryonic alcoholism programs were very cautious in interpreting and, in fact, restricting their activities to concern for alcoholism and the alcoholic exclusive of any and all other alcohol problems or issues. Alcoholism was, and is, only one of many alcohol-related problems. It is, however, if not the most obvious, perhaps the least controversial of these problems. The emergence of Alcoholics Anonymous, the highly scientific and publicized work done at Yale University, and the establishment of the National Council on Alcoholism brought significant emphasis to this health problem and made for a better atmosphere of acceptance on the part of the public. Because of these factors, alcoholism became the one—or at least the first—of the alcohol problems into which the public would tolerate governmental investigation.

In the 1940s there was a strong tendency for the establishment of state alcoholism agencies in the form of independent commissions or boards. Thomas Plaut[2] gives three major reasons for this. First was the lack of interest in alcoholism by state public health, mental health, and welfare agencies. Second was the novel and exploratory nature of governmental activity in this field; and third, the feeling that alcoholism was such a unique and different problem that totally new approaches had to be tried.

The trend beginning in the 1950s has been more toward the establishment of state programs within the states' public health or mental health departments. This trend might be interpreted as an evolutionary process, but this is not to imply that those agencies remaining as independent units are necessarily any less progressive or less effective than those which are within one or another department of government.

Twenty years of work in this field by such a wide variance of disciplines, both in the official and voluntary agencies, has produced some very healthy and meaningful results. It has been demonstrated most effectively that alcoholics can be helped through treatment. It has also been demonstrated that such effective treatment is not restricted to any particular kind or to any particular profession or combination of professions. Whether the resource is Alcoholics Anonymous, a well-informed private practitioner, or the official agency's alcoholism treatment center with its interdisciplinary team, there is a rather good batting average on the number of persons who receive significant help toward recovery. This is not to say that any of the various treatment resources or methods are interchangeable with any patient group. What proves to be helpful treatment for one patient may be contraindicated for another.

Regardless of the degree of refinement or sophistication of the various treatment techniques, it must be borne in mind that no health problem of such social complexity has been controlled by treatment alone. Official agencies were compelled to concentrate on treatment during their initial years in order to demonstrate the treatability concept. Many continue to do so today. More and more, however, are beginning, as Selden Bacon has suggested, to consider the condition of alcoholism—the process—rather than placing their primary emphasis on the needs of the alcoholic. This does not mean that official agencies are ready to quit treating alcoholics. They will continue and perhaps expand their treatment programs. More emphasis, however, will be placed on other aspects of the problem complex as time goes on—and as more of the allied professions begin to accept their role in the treatment area.

The field of alcoholism is maturing. It is maturing in its approaches to combat the illness at all levels. A more realistic view is now emerging concerning the most severe problems of alcoholism—the late stage alcoholic and the chronic court inebriate. For years attempts were made to de-emphasize the importance of the "revolving door" problem in the effort to make alcoholism a "respectable" illness. It was pointed out that the skid row alcoholic represents but a very small percentage of the alcoholic population. The rationale for this was that the public image of the alcoholic was epitomized by the skid row derelict. This image had to be changed if public awareness of the true insidious nature of the illness was to be attained. There was also another reason. There was the helpless feeling and feeling of hopelessness on the part of treatment professionals toward treating late stage alcoholism. Alcoholism is a very complex public health problem. The degree of its complexity, though, increases proportionately with its progression from early to late stage. The alcoholic who still enjoys a respectable position in the community, still lives with his family, still brings home a regular pay check, and still enjoys relatively normal physical health presents much less of a complex problem than does the one who is lacking one or more of these factors. For the former perhaps only one resource need be brought into play. Or, when more than one resource is indicated these resources can be of effective help independently of one another. Alcoholics Anonymous, or the alcoholism clinic, or the mental health clinic, or a private physician, or an understanding pastor, or a combination of these and other resources might be employed, but each one is able to provide help independently of the others. For the latter, or the ones who make up the bulk of the "revolving door" population, many resources are needed, and each resource must work closely with each and every one of the others because each is dependent on the others. The more severe the problem, the more resources necessary.

For the homeless, indigent, vocationally ill-equipped alcoholic who is in poor physical condition, such things are indicated as hospitalization, welfare, or vocational rehabilitation services in addition to therapy for his drinking problems; that is, if the diagnosis reveals that the alcoholic has suffered little or no brain damage. If he has suffered severe brain damage or is otherwise mentally inadequate to respond favorably to treatment and rehabilitation, then long-term institutional care would be indicated.

Until recent years too few people, qualified by training and inclination to be of assistance to alcoholic clients and patients, were working in these allied public agencies. Without the properly trained staffs these agencies could not be expected to be the effective team members so necessary for combating late stage alcoholism. There was, then, a real sense of hopelessness toward providing effective rehabilitation to such alcoholics having other complications.

The fact that there has been much recent activity on the part of official and voluntary agencies with regard to the chronic court inebriate indicates an emerging sense of awareness, optimism, and maturity in the field. It indicates that there are ever-increasing numbers of "alcoholism-trained people" in the allied professions. The field of alcoholism is on the threshold of a new era—an era which will see the increasing involvement of the total community resources, actively and constructively engaged in alcoholism control.

Within the governmental structure the official alcoholism agencies have, in the past, been forced to assume practically all governmental responsibility for alcohol-related problems. Now with the increasing recognition of their stakes in the problems of alcoholism, other governmental agencies are assuming more responsibility for those areas of the alcoholism problems which affect their operations. As this trend continues, the alcoholism agencies will assume more of a consultant role, more of a coordinator role, and less of an operative role, in the years ahead.

The field has grown. It has matured. Much has been accomplished in relating alcoholism with other social, legal, and medical activity. It is now time for a concerted, massive effort to implement the things which have been learned. The state and local official and voluntary agencies do not, however, possess the financial and professional resources for the kind of comprehensive push which is so necessary. The lack of facilities and manpower in this field was already severe prior to the enlightened chronic alcoholic court case decisions in the cases of *Easter* and *Driver* discussed in Chapter 9 by Peter Barton Hutt. Now that the courts have ruled that alcoholics may not be stamped as criminals and jailed for showing the symptoms of their illness in public, these shortages are acute and will become more serious when other courts render similar rulings.

No longer is the public resistant to governmental involvement in this field, and the Federal Government in the United States has been taking increasing interest in recent years and is beginning to step up its activities with regard to alcoholism. More emphasis is now being placed on the problems of alcoholism by the Vocational Rehabilitation Administration, the Welfare Administration, the Public Health Service, and the other operating agencies of the Department of Health, Education and Welfare. Former Secretary of Health, Education and Welfare, Anthony Celebrezze, established a high level committee on alcoholism in that department in 1964 with membership from each of the major constituent agencies. The purpose of this committee is to study alcoholism as it affects the nation's well-being and to make recommendations to the Secretary as to how the Department can better coordinate its own alcoholism activities while providing more significant help to the field. The National Institute of Mental Health, which has been the focal point of alcoholism activity at the Federal level, is now in the process of establishing a Center on Alcoholism which will conduct greatly expanded activity in this area.

The President has issued statements, both publicly and to Congress, indicating his interest in implementing a comprehensive program of alcoholism control at the Federal level. More than forty members of the 89th Congress introduced specific alcoholism legislation, most of which is designed to provide Federal aid to state and local alcoholism programs and to sponsor research and demonstration projects.

It is now reasonable to anticipate that the Federal government in the United States will initiate a sizeable program of alcoholism control activity in the near future. Whatever form such a Federal program will assume, it can be expected that more demands will be placed on the official state alcoholism programs to provide consultation services to other governmental and private agencies; and to act as the focal point or liaison in helping to coordinate alcoholism activity throughout the state. With adequate funds and increased numbers of trained people to cope with the problems as they relate to the entire community the time will come when the current trend of an increasing alcoholic population will be reversed.

17

International Responses to Alcoholism

ARCHER TONGUE

INTRODUCTION

From the earliest periods of recorded history until the present, government authorities have felt obliged to regulate the trade in alcoholic beverages. Until fairly recent times, however, state action has been almost exclusively concerned with legislative enactment and general regulation including such measures as that of taxation. Such legislative systems have been divided into five types:

1. *License System* in operation in Great Britain and the Netherlands.

2. *The Laissez-faire System* where there is little control, chiefly found in countries where there is a strong religious sanction against alcoholic beverages or where normal drinking is confined, very largely, to wine with meals.

3. *Prohibition,* or complete suppression of alcoholic beverages as applied in the United States of America and Finland between World War I and World War II, and now in partial application in India. Such experiments have not been successful in eliminating alcoholism.

4. *Monopoly System* in which the state owns, or directly controls all or a large part of the production, sale, and serving of alcoholic beverages and may use part of the profits to establish programs for the treatment of alcoholism and education of the public on alcohol and alcoholism.

5. *The Combined System* in which elements in the foregoing types may be combined in different system patterns.

Since World War II there has been the spread of another type of state action with regard to alcoholism; this has been the establishment of numerous overall state programs designed to set up alcoholism treatment facilities and to organize education and research. Such state programs have developed in this period in Europe, in North, Central, and South America, Australia, and elsewhere. In Europe they have tended to include the intoxication-caused problems such as alcohol and traffic, while in North America they have been chiefly occupied with alcoholism as a treatable illness, although this pattern is tending to change with the emergence of more concern for the problems of intoxication.

ALCOHOL AND ALCOHOLISM PROGRAMS: NORTH AND WESTERN EUROPE

The State Monopoly Type

Nordic alcoholism programs are represented by the countries of Norway, Sweden, and Finland. In this program type there is full or partial monopoly of alcohol beverage production and distribution with state organization of local prevention and treatment agencies throughout the country. These are the older types of national programs, dating back to the beginning of the century, in which the concept of an "alkoholpolitik" or national alcohol policy is evident.

In Finland the manufacture, importation, exportation, retail sale, and serving of alcoholic beverages and the manufacture, importation, exportation, and sale of denatured alcohol are the sole prerogative of a joint stock company in which the state holds a share-majority and absolute controlling interest. This company, *Oy Alkoholiliike Ab* (Alcohol Trade Ltd.) or ALKO, may, however, entrust the manufacture of alcoholic beverages other than brandy and the serving of alcoholic beverages to individuals and corporations to its account and for periods not exceeding three years at a time. The policy followed in the shaping of liquor sales must have in view social aims. The social principle on which the present legislation is based is defined in Article five of the Alcoholic Beverages Act: "Trade in liquor is to be organized in such a manner that at the same time as illicit trade is checked, the consumption of alcohol is brought down to the lowest possible level and drunkenness and its harmful consequences prevented."

The annual profits earned by ALKO are, after reasonable transfers to reserves and the payment to shareholders (of the present 60,000 shares all except two are held by the state) of a dividend of 7 percent on paid-up capital, to be handed over to the state for distribution in the following manner: to each commune a certain amount in reference to every inhabitant entered in the poll register in the preceding year, but only insofar as the total amount paid to the communes does not exceed 30 percent of the amount of profits handed over to the state; to the old age and disability insurance fund 35–40 percent for the augmentation of its capital; and the rest to be used for various social expenditure. The communes are required by law to utilize their amount for specific purposes, foremost among which are measures directly aimed at promoting temperance habits, the care of young persons found in a state of intoxication, and welfare measures in regard to alcoholics and their families which in this case are not to be regarded as constituting poor aid. Communes must annually submit a report of their use of the means thus received for approval by the Ministry of Social Affairs. Working within the Ministry of Social Affairs, since 1946, is an advisory commission for alcohol and alcoholism matters, the duty of which is to keep the Ministry informed and to make recommendations regarding such matters and welfare measures for alcoholics.

In 1950 the Finnish Foundation for Alcohol Studies was established. The board of the Foundation is composed of seven members who are elected once every three years. Its scientific competence is assured because at least three members of the board must be scientists. The Ministry of Education chooses one of these, and the other two are elected by the Executive Council of ALKO, which also appoints three other members. The Ministry of Social Affairs chooses the one remaining member. The Foundation has carried out pioneer sociological field research and has promoted a physiological research laboratory which acts in conjunction with the research laboratories of ALKO, the State Alcohol Monopoly. In 1953 and 1954, the Foundation opened two alcohol clinics for the purpose of experimenting with new methods of rehabilitating alcoholics. After the new methods of treatment were found to be beneficial, this activity was transferred to the A-clinic Foundation, which was especially established for that purpose. A special "hangover" clinic was opened in Helsinki, "the hangover" being regarded as meriting particular attention and treatment. The results of research supported by the Foundation have been published in both Finnish and English in the series "Alcohol Research in the Northern Countries."

The Ministry of Social Affairs is responsible for the supervision of the beverage alcohol trade in its entirety, in particular the manufacture of alcohol for industrial and similar purposes. Nearly every municipality appoints a board concerned with alcohol and alcoholism questions in its area, and to guide these boards the Ministry of Social Affairs employs seven district advisors with a chief advisor to supervise. The

general educational work is supplemented by that of private
organizations which also receive financial grants through the
Ministry of Social Affairs.

In Norway in 1936 a body known as the State Temperance
Council was created consisting of five members appointed
by the King. This body is responsible for ensuring liaison
between different State departments on legislative and administrative matters concerning alcoholism. Its major activity,
however, is that of helping and guiding the municipal Sobriety
Boards which are established in almost all areas in Norway
and have as their duty the care of alcoholics and the promotion of education on alcohol problems. In particular the State
Temperance Council arranges courses for the orientation of
these committees in their duties. Then the State Temperance
Council maintains liaison between the Ministry and the various private Temperance education bodies who receive grants
from the State for education and research. One of the most
important of these is the State Board of Temperance Education which was actually set up as long ago as 1902, and which
in addition to representatives of private bodies includes in
its management board representatives of the Social Affairs
Ministry, the Ecclesiastical and Educational Ministry, the
Central Board of Statistics, and the University of Oslo.

The State obtains large receipts from the sale of alcohol
in the country—at the moment more than 500 million crowns
annually whilst the annual expenditure by consumers on alcoholic drinks reaches 780 million crowns. In Norway the sale
of alcohol is in large part under monopoly. There is a government company, A/S Vinmonopolet, which possesses the exclusive right of importing wines and spirits, as well as the
monopoly for the sale and retail of spirits. The profit received
by the Monopoly goes directly into the State Treasury after
the company has paid to the State large taxes on the sale. A
part of the Monopoly receipts is given over to social purposes,
above all to combating tuberculosis. The law provides that
20 percent of the taxes payable for the permit to sell and
retail spirits and 20 percent of the profits of the monopoly
must go to a fund, called the Temperance Fund, which is
devoted to the encouragement of work to combat alcoholism.

Each year this fund receives more than 4 million crowns. The fund must, however, cover the ordinary parliamentary grants from the national budget for general educational work on alcohol and alcoholism and support the sanatoria and other facilities. At present there are about one million crowns left which can be used for special undertakings, e.g., for the construction of a home for alcoholics, a work-home, and so forth. These funds are not available directly to the service's administrators. It is Parliament which decides the amount to be used from the fund. For information and education on alcoholism the State allows annually about one million crowns. In this sum are included the expenditure of the State Temperance Council for its administration, the subsidy given to the National Temperance Education Board, and a contribution of about 200,000 crowns for the private organizations carrying on activities of an educational character.

In Sweden the State program regarding alcohol and alcoholism may be considered under three heads: (1) the manufacture and sale of alcoholic beverages, (2) education on alcohol and alcoholism questions, and (3) the treatment of alcoholics. In addition great importance is attached to research on alcohol problems, and a special department of alcohol research has been set up in the famous Karolinska Institute under the direction of Professor L. Goldberg. Swedish legislation distinguishes between strong alcoholic beverages (spirits, liqueurs, wines, and strong beer) and ordinary beer. The retailing of strong alcoholic beverages may take place only in special shops which are managed by the state sales company. The sale of strong drinks is concentrated in the hands of monopoly companies in which the state has decisive influence. There is one such company for wholesale trade and another for retail trade. An important rule is that as far as possible the motive of private profit should be removed from the selling of strong alcoholic beverages. On the other hand, the profit element as a rule remains with regard to the production and sale of beer. For the serving of beer, however, there are certain so called "public utility" companies which carry on their work without the aim of profit and which hand over any profits for purposes of public interest.

The elimination of the private profit interest extends also to the serving of spirituous liquors in restaurants; these places are only allowed to receive a compensation which is estimated to equal their costs of serving spirituous liquors. This compensation consists of 15 percent of the value of what is served, but there is a limitation which means that compensation will not be paid for sales of spirituous liquors above a certain level. The limit has been fixed on the basis that the quantity of spirituous liquors served should be in a reasonable proportion to the sales of food, non-alcoholic beverages, and beer. The prices of spirituous liquors in restaurants are fixed by an authority called the *Kontrollstyrelsen*. For the serving of wines there is no such limitation of profit but the *Kontrollstyrelsen* has to exercise a certain supervision of the pricing of wines. For strong beers the *Kontrollstyrelsen* fixes maximum prices.

The educational program is under the supervision of the Government Board of Education which is responsible for school instruction, publication of guides for teachers, and distribution of financial aid to voluntary organizations carrying on educational work outside the schools. In addition there is a Central Temperance Education Board which works in cooperation with the Board of Education. This body is directed by a committee consisting of 12 persons. Half of these are appointed by the Government which also nominates the chairman; affiliated organizations appoint the other half. The Government members represent scientific research and a number of large popular movements such as the trade unions, the salaried employee's associations, and the adult education, free church, and sports movements. According to its status the Board of Education is the supervisory authority for the Central Temperance Education Board but the latter has considerable freedom to organize its work and carry on its tasks. It is neutral in controversial religious and political—including temperance policy—questions.

A cooperation committee with the aim of stimulating education and information in the schools was formed in 1959 on the initiative of the Board of Education. On this committee there are representatives of the Board of Education, the

Temperance Education Board, and the National Association of Parents and Teachers, as well as a school welfare officer. The committee tries to make available more concrete and interesting educational material. Another important part of the educational program is cooperation with the parent-teacher associations at the schools. The committee tries in various ways to encourage these associations to include the alcohol problem in their programs; proposals for special educational material for such associations have been prepared.

The Temperance Education Board pays for a large number of lectures which give unbiased information on the alcohol problem. Quite a number are held in such organizations as trade unions, political clubs, schools, and military units. It also distributes material to the press concerning new scientific data on the alcohol problem in the hope that this information—which is published by a large number of papers—may have some educational effect in reducing alcohol habits. In addition, private temperance organizations receive subsidies: (1) in proportion to their membership; (2) for the larger societies grants for one or more instructors approved by the Board of Education on the alcohol problem; and (3) special grants for informational activities.

The treatment of alcoholics in Sweden is supervised by the National Social Welfare Board through local and county agencies for the prevention and treatment of alcoholism. The local prevention and treatment agencies consist of at least five members, one of whom if possible should be a doctor. Its chief tasks are as follows: general activities for the promotion of sobriety in the area, the giving of advice and information in connection with the tasks of the committee, the provision of individual, psychologically suitable treatment aimed at removing the reasons for alcohol abuse and the taking into care of alcohol-abusers of different kinds, and also the handling of problems concerning road traffic and alcohol (driving licenses). The county prevention and treatment agencies, besides undertaking tasks similar to those of the local committees, have also to supervise and help the local committees. The state defrays 75 percent of the costs of the local agencies and the total cost of the county agencies.

The state also runs public institutions for the treatment of alcoholics and defrays a large part of the cost of treatment in private institutions of a convalescent-home type. The City of Stockholm itself has a comprehensive service of alcoholism information and treatment. The city prevention and treatment agency operates through 22 district offices plus a central information center. Half-way houses and treatment homes are maintained. In association with the hospital service two polyclinics and two hospital departments are at its disposal. There are two medical consultation centers and an emergency telephone help service available. There is an education service for personnel training and general information activity. In addition there is a university alcoholism clinic where special emphasis is laid on research.

The Mixed Type

The second type of program may be referred to as the mixed type since it includes both public and private enterprise in the field of alcohol and alcoholism problems. Switzerland, the Netherlands, and Austria may be taken as examples.

In Switzerland, executive authority resides in the cantons, and in some of these alcoholism prevention and treatment programs have been set up, sometimes in the cantonal health department, as example the alcoholism prophylaxy office in the Canton of Vaud and the Socio-Medical Service for alcoholics in the Canton of Lucerne. In the latter program there is a close liaison with the traffic police authorities. This results in investigations of traffic accidents in which alcoholic intoxication has played a part in order to ascertain if alcoholics needing treatment are involved.

On the federal level of Switzerland a commission was set up in 1945. This commission initiates research, advises regarding alcoholism treatment programs, examines health and dietary questions as they are related to alcohol consumption, and watches over the use made by the cantons of their share of the receipts of the Alcohol Administration which controls distillation and taxation of distilled beverages. Private bodies concerned with alcoholism education and treatment are represented in the Federal Commission and receive federal and cantonal subsidies. An example of its activities is the circulation of a guide on alcoholism to all medical practitioners in the country.

In the Netherlands the care of alcoholics is almost entirely in the hands of medico-social consultation bureaus or, as they may be described, out-patient alcoholism clinics. There are 19 of these—15 of them having been set up since World War II. Most of them are incorporated bodies, the usual organization being that of a society which is responsible for the bureau. The executive board is responsible for personnel and finance but has no function as regards the practical work. The director of the bureau is the executive officer and is always a social worker. His staff is composed of between one and ten social workers and one or several part-time psychiatrists and physicians, and, sometimes, with a part-time psychologist. There is close cooperation with Alcoholics Anonymous. There is emphasis on the role of the social worker. Assistance is rendered to alcoholics in the first instance by those whose expertness consists of conscious sytematized knowledge of human interrelationships in all their diversity and degree of skill in handling these relationships. The social worker's activity focuses both on the client and on the client's environment—on the environment either to activate aid sources in it or to change it and on the client to lend him the sociopsychological support he needs.

Financing of the bureaus comes from government departments, provinces and municipalities, and from private sources. There is an advisory committee in the Ministry of Social Affairs representing the different groups concerned with alcohol problems, i.e., the ministries concerned, local authorities, treatment centers, the alcohol beverage industry, and the Temperance Movement.

In Austria there is also an advisory committee on alcoholism in the Ministry of Social Affairs. The City of Vienna has its own alcoholism treatment services; and provincial health departments also provide services. Private bodies receive government subsidies for their work in the field of alcoholism.

The Integrated Type

Another type of program has its treatment program integrated within the Ministry of Public Health with independent official and private bodies responsible for prevention and education. An example of this type is France. In 1955 it was decided that mental health dispensaries throughout France should be made responsible for the alcoholism treatment programs. These bodies were charged with the case finding of alcoholics, outpatient treatment, and after-care of those treated in hospital. The state was made responsible for 83 percent of the maintenance cost of this service in order to facilitate its development, the remaining expenses to be borne by the local administration. The following principles guide this program:

1. Psychiatric orientation of the consultative service.
2. Prolonged and thorough medical contact with the patient.
3. Interdisciplinary cooperation by means of a medico-social team.
4. The exclusion of authoritarian or repressive methods.
5. Close liaison between the director of the out-patient clinic (dispensary) and the medical practitioners.
6. Close liaison between the outpatient clinic and the hospital services.
7. Clinic outpatient consultations are free of charge to patients.

A program of particular interest is that of the 13th District of Paris, where the principle is practiced of the same interdisciplinary team following the patient in all the different establishments to which he is sent, such as the outpatient consultation, the day-hospital, the therapeutic workshop, and the psychiatric hospital itself.

A state program for informing the public on a nation-wide basis is found in the activities of the High Committee of Study and Information on Alcoholism in France, dating from 1954. The terms of reference of this committee, which is directly responsible to the Prime Minister, are to assemble all information relative to the problem of alcoholism, to propose to the Government any measures which would tend to the diminution of this problem, to undertake with other interested bodies an extensive campaign of information directed to the general public, to public authorities, large public utilities, and so forth, on the dangers of alcoholism and the possibilities of arresting its development. The members who are elected in their own right are not more than 18, and consist of three doctors, two members of the teaching service, five members of Parliament, or former Parliament members, several high officials, an industrialist, an agriculturalist, a manual worker, and a journalist. There is a permanent panel of 13 experts called into consultation on the different subjects under examination as required. There are broadly three fields of activity: (1) general information; (2) modification of the production of alcoholic beverages, as, for instance, dealing with problems posed by the prevalence of home-distilling, the elimination of wines of poor quality, and the encouragement of non-alcoholic beverages; and (3) the harmonization of the policies of different ministerial departments with regard to alcoholism. The cooperation between this Committee and the Ministry of Health, with its particular program for the treatment and rehabilitation of alcoholics, is close. A continuing feature of the Committee's activity has been the promotion of research in a variety of fields which have included such diverse subjects as the effects of alcohol on the human organism, the occurrence of factory accidents due to alcoholism, and regional surveys on alcoholism incidence. A private, subsidized body in France, the National Committee of Defense Against Alcoholism, carries out a national information service working through departmental or regional committees throughout the country.

ALCOHOL AND ALCOHOLISM PROGRAMS: EASTERN EUROPE

Several countries of Eastern Europe have evolved state programs on alcohol problems and alcoholism in the last few years. In Poland a National Committee Against Alcoholism was established, subsidized by the Ministry of Health and operating through regional committees, to inform the public on the question and to organize treatment facilities throughout the country. In 1957, the state program was supplemented by an Interministerial Commission on Alcoholism. One of the outstanding problems in a number of countries is the question of harmonizing the policies followed by the governmental departments which are responsible for the production and sale of alcoholic beverages and those which deal with alcohol problems and alcoholism. Moreover, there are numerous government departments whose activities touch alcohol and alcoholism problems at some point. This Interministerial Commission in Poland was composed of the vice-ministers of nine Ministries concerned in some way with alcoholism problems, under the leadership of the Minister of Labour and Social Service.

The task of this Commission was to work out an overall plan for dealing with alcoholism, and this has gradually led up to the important legislation promulgated in recent years. This legislation which covers the reorganization of the treatment of alcoholics as well as taxation of alcoholic beverages and includes such detailed questions as the conditions of sale and consumption of alcoholic beverages on boats is comprehensive, and the directives to implement its operation are drawn up by the appropriate ministries, Health, Labour, Communications, Marine, and so forth. Under this legislation the Districts People's Councils are to implement measures for dealing with alcoholism and also to render the necessary assistance to the Social Committees Against Alcoholism and other social groups in the organizing and conducting of a campaign of instruction and education on the subject. These Councils after consultation with the Social Committees Against Alcoholism are to allocate funds amounting to at least 10 percent of the excise revenues they receive from alcoholic beverages for the purpose of combating alcoholism. It is the duty of the provincial people's councils to organize and operate inpatient health service establishments for habitual alcoholics, and for the district and municipal people's councils to organize and operate outpatient health service establishments for habitual alcoholics. A particular feature is the sobering up stations where drunken persons found in the streets by the police are lodged for the night at their own expense.

In the Ministry of Health in Czechoslovakia a Central Committee to devise an overall program to deal with alcohol and alcoholism programs was set up in 1957, following a government directive of September, 1956. It is at one and the same time a consultative, initiating, coordinating, and control organization. Its members are representatives of the Ministries of Health, Home Affairs, Justice, Education and Culture, the food industry, domestic trade, the State Planning Authority, the national youth organizations, the Red Cross, trade unions, and women's organizations. Its work is carried on through four commissions, one dealing with the development and encouragement of the production of nonalcoholic beverages, a second with the protection of children and young people from the effects of alcohol abuse, a third for legislative proposals, and a fourth for scientific research. The objects of this program are to combat alcoholism by the following means: (1) through the education of the people to moderation by instruction on the causes and results of alcoholism and through the treatment of those persons whose health has been harmed by it; (2) through the reduction in the sale of alcoholic beverages to certain categories of persons or on certain conditions; and (3) through the punishment by the courts or the national district committees of violation of the various alcoholism control laws.

In 1954, in the Soviet Union a directive was sent out by the Ministry of Health requiring doctors and health personnel, physicians as well as psychiatrists, to undertake an educative action on the subject of alcoholism. This program has been developed into a nation-wide program by the Ministry through the Central Institute of Scientific Research on Health Education. This Institute is the center which undertakes scientific research on methods to be applied in the education of the public on alcoholism. In this task it is aided by a consultative commission against alcoholism. The educational program on alcoholism is closely linked with the program of treatment and rehabilitation of alcoholics since those engaged in the latter sphere also have an important part in the educational program. Some of the principles of this program are the following: The health education work must first of all emphasize that abuse of alcohol and drunkenness cannot be tolerated, that alcoholism is treatable, and the wish of the alcoholic to be cured is of paramount importance. As in most countries alcoholism is recognized as an illness, but it is emphasized that alcoholics must not always be regarded as patients, for that would imply condoning their antisocial behavior and indicating doubt of their responsibility for their actions. There is a tendency in some countries to separate as two distinctive programs prevention measures and treatment facilities. In the Soviet program treatment and rehabilitation are also used as means of effective education on alcoholism and the treatment program in itself performs an important public educational service.

In Hungary a National Commission on Alcoholism representative of governmental ministries, national organizations, and professions was created by the Ministry of Health and the Red Cross in 1962. The Bulgarian Red Cross has been actively working with alcoholism problems for many years, and in 1966 a National Commission on Alcoholism was appointed. In Yugoslavia the Red Cross has operated a national program since 1954.

ALCOHOL AND ALCOHOLISM PROGRAMS: CANADA

In 1949, the first Canadian program, the Alcoholism Research Foundation, was set up in the Province of Ontario. The Foundation is charged with conducting a program of research on alcoholism, and provision is made for agreements with universities and hospitals for experimentation on methods of treatment as well as for the setting up of clinics and centers and the general dissemination of information. In 1965, the Foundation was entrusted with the whole area of the alcoholism problem by the Ontario Legislation. Drug dependency also comes within its activity. The Foundation has a wide area of activity in such diverse areas as consumption statistics, sales trends, the alcohol language, as well as alcoholism treatment and research. In addition, the Ontario Alcoholism Research Foundation has developed international exchange of research workers which began with an exchange between the Foundation and the Finnish Foundation of Alcohol Studies. It should be noted that alcoholism programs exist in all of Canada's provinces.

ALCOHOL AND ALCOHOLISM PROGRAMS: CENTRAL AND SOUTH AMERICA

In Central America the treatment programs in Guatemala and Costa Rica deserve mention. The "Patronato" in Guatemala to combat alcoholism was launched as a private body in 1945, but, following the law of 1949, received increased state support and has developed a comprehensive program of prevention and treatment. In Costa Rica there is a Commission on Alcoholism depending in part on the state and in part on voluntary support. In addition to medical and social services the Commission has carried out epidemiological and ecological research. Elsewhere in Latin America various types of programs were put into operation, as, for instance, that growing out of the Commission on Delinquency of the Ministry of Justice in Venezuela, and the program organized by the Ministry of Health in Peru stimulated by the National Conference on Alcoholism held there in 1957. In Chile over some years there has been a developing program with particular emphasis on research.

ALCOHOL AND ALCOHOLISM PROGRAMS: AUSTRALIA

In Australia each state has developed its own individual program. In Queensland, in 1963, a coordinating committee on alcoholism was appointed consisting of the Director Generals of Health and Education, senior officers of both these Departments, and officers of the Health Education Council. In 1963, the Tasmanian State Government appointed a Welfare Officer and Counsellor on Alcoholism in the Division of Psychiatric Services, and an Alcoholism Information Center was opened. The Government of Western Australia deals with the problem through an Inebriates Advisory Board. Official policy in South Australia has been influenced by the Swedish system, and in that state as well as in Victoria, there is an independent Alcoholism Foundation. In Victoria it combats alcoholism by means of medicine, sociology, education, and research. Finally, New South Wales has its Foundation for Research and Treatment of Alcoholism with a wide multi-disciplinary approach to the question.

CONCLUSION

In conclusion, mention could be made of many other programs which have developed since 1960. The alcoholism treatment units in Great Britain set up under Ministry of Health directive by Regional Hospital Boards, the consultation and treatment centers in Spain, and the extensive program comprising eleven treatment centers of different types, both outpatient and inpatient, operated by the Administration of the Province of Milan in Italy.

NOTES

1. International Overview: Social and Cultural Factors in Drinking Patterns, Pathological and Nonpathological
David J. Pittman

[1] Spindler, George D., "Alcoholism Symposium: Editorial Preview," *American Anthropologist*, 66:341, 1964.

[2] *Expert Committee on Mental Health, Alcoholism Subcommittee, Second Report*, World Health Org. Techn. Rep. Ser., No. 48, August, 1952.

[3] Azayem, G. M., "The Problem of Alcoholism in Egypt," in *Proceedings of the 25th International Congress Against Alcoholism*, Lausanne, Switzerland: Bureau International Contre L'Alcoolisme, 1956, pp. 1–5.

[4] Israel, Chad, "The Present Situation in India," in *Proceedings of the 25th International Congress Against Alcoholism*, Lausanne, Switzerland, Bureau International contre L'Alcoolisme, 1956, pp. 1–6.

[5] Fryer, Peter, *Mrs. Grundy: Studies in English Prudery*, New York: London House and Maxwell, 1963, p. 132.

[6] Lemert, Edwin M., "Forms and Pathology of Drinking in Three Polynesian Societies," *American Anthropologist*, 66:361–374, 1964. Also, Madsen, William, "The Alcoholic Agringado," *American Anthropologist*, pp. 355–361.

[7] Pittman, David J., and Sterne, Muriel W., *The Carousel: Hospitals, Social Agencies, and the Alcoholic*, Report presented to the Missouri Division of Health, 1962, p. 25.

[8] Myerson, Abraham, "Alcohol: A Study of Social Ambivalence," *Quart. J. Stud. Alc.*, 1:13–20, 1940.

[9] Skolnick, Jerome H., "Religious Affiliation and Drinking Behavior," *Quart. J. Stud. Alc.*, 19:452–470, 1958.

[10] Bales, Robert F., "Attitudes Toward Drinking in the Irish Culture," in Pittman, D. J., and Snyder, C. R. (eds.), *Society, Culture, and Drinking Patterns*, New York: John Wiley & Sons, 1962, p. 184.

[11] Riley, J. W., and Marden, C. F., "The Social Pattern of Alcoholic Drinking," *Quart. J. Stud. Alc.*, 8:265–273, 1947.

[12] Snyder, Charles R., *Alcohol and the Jews*, Glencoe, Ill.: The Free Press, 1958.

[13] Lolli, Giorgio, *et al.*, *Alcohol and Italian Culture*, Glencoe, Ill.: The Free Press, 1958.

[14] Bales, Freed, "Cultural Differences in Rates of Alcoholism," *Quart. J. Stud. Alc.*, 6:480–499, 1946.

[15] Sadoun, Roland and Lolli, Giorgio, "Choice of Alcoholic Beverage Among 120 Alcoholics in France," *Quart. J. Stud. Alc.*, 23:449–458, 1962.

[16] Moore, Robert A., "Alcoholism in Japan," *Quart. J. Stud. Alc.*, 25:142–150, 1964.

[17] Heath, Dwight B., "Drinking Patterns of the Bolivian Camba," in Pittman and Snyder (eds.), *Society, Culture, and Drinking Patterns, op. cit.*, pp. 25–26.

[18] Bastide, H., "Public Opinion," in McCarthy, Raymond G. (ed.), *Drinking and Intoxication*, Glencoe, Ill.: The Free Press, 1959, pp. 158–159.

[19] Fouquet, Pierre, "Facteurs Socio-Culturels et Économiques de L'Alcoolisme," Conférence donnée au Cours Européen d'été sur L'-Alcoolisme, Lausanne, Switzerland, June, 1963, no page.

[20] Srisastaua, Shanker, *Juvenile Vagrancy*, New York: Asia Publishing House, 1963, p. 68.

[21] Gadourek, Ivan, *Riskante Gewoonten en Zorg Voor Eigen Welzijn*, Groningen, The Netherlands: J. B. Walters, 1963. Also summary in *Report of the 7th Summer Institute of Scientific Studies for the Prevention and Treatment of Alcoholism, June 12–23, 1961*, Amsterdam, Leyden: A. W. Sythoff, no date, pp. 19–22.

[22] Knupfer, Genevieve, *Characteristics of Abstainers: A Comparison of Drinkers and Non-Drinkers in a Large California City*, Berkeley, California: Department of Public Health, November, 1961.

[23] Swiecicki, Andrzej, "Survey on Alcohol Consumption in Poland," *Archives of Criminology*, Vol. II, Warsaw: Department of Criminology, Institute of Legal Sciences, Polish Academy of Science, 1964, pp. 385–391.

[24] McDouall, Robin, "Change and Decay," in Cyril Ray (ed.), *The Compleat Imbiber 6*, New York: Erikson, 1963, p. 10.

[25] David, Elizabeth, "Gin and Whisky in the Kitchen," in Cyril Ray (ed.), *The Compleat Imbiber 6*, New York: Erikson, 1963, pp. 153–157.

[26] Bonfiglio, Giovanni, "The Characteristics of Alcoholism in Italy," III Symposium of the Automobile Club on "Alcoholism and Alimentation," Salsomagior, Italy, May 24, 1963, pp. 1–13.

[27] For a more complete discussion of this point, see Chotlos, John W., and Deiter, John, "Psychological Consideration in the Etiology of Alcoholism," in Pittman, David J. (ed.), *Alcoholism: An Interdisciplinary Approach*, Springfield, Ill.: Charles T. Thomas, 1959, pp. 16–31.

[28] Vodraska, Rudolf, "Ideas on the Health Consciousness of Youth as Regards Alcoholism Questions," Lecture presented at the Summer Institute of Scientific Studies for the Prevention and the Treatment of Alcoholism, Warsaw, Poland, June, 1962.

[29] Pfautz, Harold W., "Alcohol in Popular Fiction," *Quart. J. Stud. Alc.*, 23:131–146, 1962.

[30] Pittman, David J., and Tongue, Archer (eds.), *Handbook of Organizations for Research on Alcohol and Alcoholism Problems*, Lausanne, Switzerland: International Council on Alcohol and Alcoholism, 1964, p. 37.

[31] Maddox, George, "Teenage Drinking in the United States," in Pittman and Snyder (eds.), *Society, Culture, and Drinking Patterns, op. cit.*, pp. 230–245.

[32] Block, Marvin, "Latest on Over-Drinking," *U.S. News and World Report*, June 15, 1964, p. 55.

[33] Dollard, John, "Drinking Mores of the Social Classes," in *Alcohol, Science, and Society*, New Haven: Journal of Studies on Alcohol, 1945.

[34] Gusfield, Joseph R. "Status Conflicts and the Changing Ideologies of the American Temperance Movement," in Pittman and Snyder (eds.), *Society, Culture, and Drinking Patterns, op. cit.*, pp. 101–121.

[35] Riesman, David, Potter, Robert J., and Watson, Jeanne, "The Vanishing Host," *Hum. Org.*, 19:17–27, 1960.

[36] Otterland, Anders, "Alcohol and the Merchant Seafarer," 26th International Congress on Alcohol and Alcoholism, Stockholm, Sweden: August 1–5, 1960, *Abstracts*, pp. 206–207.

[37] Bonfiglio, G., and Cicala, S., "L'alcoholismonei marittinni italiani," from Records of the Center of Studies and Research for Health and Social Welfare of Seamen, CIRM, Rome, 1963, pp. 53–65.

2. The Human Body and Alcohol
Joseph B. Kendis

[1] "Alcohol Education in Oregon Schools," State Department of Education, Salem, Oregon, pp. 18–25.

[2] "Drunkenness, Drinking, and Driving," "Teenage Drinking," "Alcoholism, A Manual for Students on Alcohol Problems," Bureau on Alcoholism, Regina, Saskatchewan, Canada.

[3] Greenberg, Leon A., "Alcohol in the Body," in McCarthy, R. G., 1st edition, *Drinking and Intoxication*, Glencoe, Illinois: Illinois Free Press, 1959, pp. 7–13.

[4] Himwich, Harold E., The Physiology of Alcohol," *Manual on Alcoholism*, American Medical Association, Chicago, Illinois, 1962.

[5] Ishee, Vashti, "The Relation of Alcoholic Beverages to the Development of Healthy Individuals," *Mississippi Science Supplement*, State Department of Education, Jackson, Mississippi.

[6] Keller, Mark, "How Alcohol Affects the Body," New Brunswick, New Jersey: Rutgers Center of Alcohol Studies, 1955.

[7] Kendis, Joseph B., "Treatment of Acute Alcoholism in Private Practice and Hospital Surroundings," Published as part of a Symposium by New Hampshire State Program on Alcoholism, 1962.

[8] Kinard, Fred W., "Alcohol and the Human Body," *Proceedings, Third Southeastern School of Alcohol Studies, 1963*, University of Georgia Center for Continuing Education, Athens, Georgia, pp. 31–37.

[9] Walker, J. F., "Alcohol and the Human Body," *Basic Papers, First Southeastern School of Alcohol Studies, 1961*, Millsaps College, Jackson, Mississippi, pp. 16–24.

[10] "When Ethyl Takes the Wheel," Michigan State Board of Alcoholism and Michigan Alcohol Education Foundation, Lansing, Michigan.

3. Psychiatric Aspects of Alcoholism
Ronald J. Catanzaro

[1] Jellinek, E. M., *Disease Concept of Alcoholism*, New Haven, Conn.: United Printing Services, 1960.

[2] Jellinek, E. M., "Cultural Differences in the Meaning of Alcoholism," in Pittman, D. J., and Snyder, C. R. (eds.), *Society, Culture, and Drinking Patterns*, New York: John Wiley & Sons, Inc., 1962, pp. 382–394.

[3] Catanzaro, R. J., "Rehabilitation of the Incarcerated Alcoholic Offender," in *Selected Papers*, 15th Annual NAAAP Meeting, Portland, Oregon, September 27–October 1, 1964, pp. 161–170.

[4] Smith, J. J., "A Medical Approach to the Problem Drinker," *Quart. J. Stud. Alc.*, 10:251–257, 1949.

[5] Diethelm, O. (ed.), *Etiology of Chronic Alcoholism*, Springfield, Ill.: Charles C. Thomas, 1955.

[6] Clinebell, H. J., Jr., *Understanding and Counseling the Alcoholic*, Nashville: Abingdon Press, 1956.

[7] Robins, L. N., Bates, W., and O'Neal, P., "Adult Drinking Patterns of Former Problem Children," in Pittman, D. J., and Snyder, C. R. (eds.), *op. cit.*, pp. 395–412.

[8] Amark, C. A., *Study in Alcoholism*, Copenhagen: Ejnar Murchsgaard, 1951.

[9] Catanzaro, R. J., "A One Man Team Approach for the Treatment of Alcoholics," *Military Medicine*, Vol. 129, No. 7, July, 1964.

[10] Jellinek, E. M., "Phases of Alcohol Addiction," in Pittman, D. J., and Snyder, C. R. (eds.), *op. cit.*, pp. 356–368.

4. No References

5. Teen-agers, Drinking, and the Law: A Study of Arrest Trends for Alcohol-Related Offenses
Muriel W. Sterne
David J. Pittman
Thomas Coe

[1] Pittman, D. J., and Gordon, C. W., *Revolving Door: A Study of the Chronic Police Case Inebriate*, Glencoe, Ill.: The Free Press, 1958.

[2] "Liquor law violation" does not necessarily entail excessive drinking by the offender.

[3] Glad, D. D., "Attitudes and Experiences of American-Jewish and American-Irish Youth as Related to Differences in Adult Rates of Inebriety," *Quart. J. Stud. Alc.*, December 1957, pp. 406–472.

[4] Lolli, G., Serianni, E., Golder, G., and Luzzatto-Pegiz, P., *Alcohol in Italian Culture*, Glencoe, Ill.: The Free Press and Yale Center of Alcohol Studies, 1958.

[5] Maddox, G. L., "Teenage Drinking in the United States," in Pittman, D. J., and Snyder, C. R. (eds.), *Society, Culture and Drinking Patterns*, New York: John Wiley & Sons, 1962.

[6] Snyder, C. R., *Alcohol and the Jews,* Glencoe, Ill.: The Free Press and Yale Center of Alcohol Studies, 1958.

[7] Straus, R., and Bacon, S. D., *Drinking in College,* New Haven, Conn.: Yale University Press, 1953.

[8] Data on teen-age drinking reported below are derived from Maddox' synthesis of research findings on over 8,000 high-school students throughout the country.

[9] *New York State Moreland Commission on the Alcoholic Beverage Control,* Interim Report to the Governor, August 30, 1963, p. 4.

[10] Fagan E. R., "The Tavern and the Juvenile Delinquent," unpublished master's thesis, University of Wisconsin, 1953.

[11] This age grouping, rather than twenty and under, would account for the majority of alcohol-related offenses attributable to youth.

[12] On October 13, 1965, a "breath test" for intoxication went into effect in Missouri, but is currently being tested in the courts.

[13] From 1950 to 1960, there was a 15 per cent decrease in the number of persons aged seventeen to twenty and a 20 per cent decrease in the number of persons twenty-one and over.

[14] Missouri Revised Statutes 311–020 and 312–010.

6. Drinking Patterns and Alcoholism Among American Negroes
Muriel W. Sterne

[1] Jellinek, E. M., *The Disease Concept of Alcoholism,* New Haven: Hillhouse Press, 1960. See especially pp. 36–39.

[2] Jellinek, E. M., "Cultural Differences in the Meaning of Alcoholism," ch. 22 in Pittman, David J., and Snyder, C. R. (eds.), *Society, Culture and Drinking Patterns,* N.Y.: John Wiley & Sons, Inc., 1962.

[3] Pittman, D. J., and Gordon, C. W., *Revolving Door: A Study of the Chronic Police Case Inebriate,* Glencoe, Ill.: Free Press, 1958.

[4] McCarthy, R. G., (ed.), *Drinking and Intoxication,* Glencoe, Ill.: The Free Press, 1959. See Part III, Drinking Practices, U.S.A.

[5] Pittman and Snyder, *op. cit.* See Section III, Social Structure, Subcultures, and Drinking Patterns.

[6] Mulford, H. A., and Miller, D. E., "Drinking in Iowa. II, The Extent of Drinking and Selected Sociocultural Categories," *Quart. J. Stud. Alc.* 21:26–39, 1960.

[7] Knupfer, G., *et al., California Drinking Practices Study,* Report No. 6, Factors Related to Amount of Drinking in An Urban Community, Berkeley: California State Department of Public Health, 1963.

[8] Knupfer, G., *California Drinking Practices Study,* Report No. 3, Revised, Characteristics of Abstainers, Berkeley: California State Department of Public Health, 1961.

[9] Mulford, Harold A., "Drinking and Deviant Drinking, U. S. A., 1963," *Quart. J. Stud. Alc.* 25:634–650, 1964.

[10] Pittman, D. J. (ed.), *Alcoholism, An Interdisciplinary Approach,* Springfield, Ill.: Charles C. Thomas, 1959. See Section I, "Research in the Etiology of Alcoholism."

[11] Bales, R. F., "Cultural Differences in Rates of Alcoholism," *Quart. J. Stud. Alc.* 6:480–499, 1946.

12 Snyder, C. R., *Alcohol and the Jews*, Glencoe, Ill.: Free Press, 1958.

13 Bales, R. F., "Attitudes toward Drinking in the Irish Culture," Ch. 10 in Pittman and Snyder, *op. cit.*

14 Glad, D. D., "Attitudes and Experiences of American-Jewish and American-Irish Male Youth as Related to Differences in Adult Rates of Inebriety," *Quart. J. Stud. Alc.* 8:406–472, 1947.

15 Madsen, W., "The Alcoholic Agringado," *Am. Anthrop.* 66:355–360, 1964.

16 Thorner, I., "Ascetic Protestantism and Alcoholism," *Psychiatry* 16:167–176, 1953.

17 Straus, R., and Bacon, S., *Drinking in College*, New Haven: Yale University Press, 1953.

18 Skolnick, J. H., "Religious Affiliation and Drinking Behavior," *Quart. J. Stud. Alc.* 19:452–470, 1958.

19 Lemert, E. M., *Alcohol and the Northwest Coast Indians*, Berkeley: University of California Publications in Culture and Society 2:303–406, 1954.

20 Trice, H. M., "Alcoholism: Group Factors in Etiology and Therapy," *Hum. Org.* 15:33–40, 1956.

21 Heath, D., "Drinking Patterns of the Bolivian Camba," Ch. 2 in Pittman and Snyder, *op. cit.*

22 "Cultural consistency" has been intuitively apprehended in the alcohol literature. Its lack of conceptual definition may account for some of the disagreement surrounding Ullman's formulation.

23 Ullman, A. D., "Sociocultural Backgrounds of Alcoholism," *Ann. Amer. Acad. Pol. Soc. Sci.* 315:48–54, 1958.

24 Myerson, A., "Alcohol: A Study of Social Ambivalence," *Quart. J. Stud. Alc.* 1:13–20, 1940.

25 Bacon, S., "Social Settings Conducive to Alcoholism: A Sociological Approach to a Medical Problem," *J. Am. Med. Assn.* 164:177–181, 1957.

26 Lolli, G., *et al.*, *Alcohol in Italian Culture*, Glencoe, Ill.: Free Press, 1958.

27 Barnett, M. L., "Alcoholism in the Cantonese of New York City: An Anthropological Study," in O. Diethelm (ed.), *Etiology of Chronic Alcoholism*, Springfield, Ill.: Charles C. Thomas, 1955.

28 Mangin, W., "Drinking Among Andean Indians," *Quart J. Stud. Alc.* 18:55–65, 1957.

29 Netting, R. McC., "Beer As A Locus of Value Among the West African Kofyar," *Am. Anthrop.* 66:375–384, 1964.

30 Lemert, E. M., "Forms and Pathology of Drinking in Three Polynesian Societies," *Am. Anthrop.* 66:361–374, 1964.

31 Simmons, O. G., "Ambivalence and the Learning of Drinking Behavior in a Peruvian Community," Ch. 3 in Pittman and Snyder, *op. cit.*

32 Franklin, J. H., *From Slavery to Freedom*, Rev. Ed., N. Y.: Alfred A. Knopf, 1956.

33 Guild, J. F., *Black Laws of Virginia*, Richmond: Whittel & Shepperson, 1936.

34 Wiley, B., *Southern Negroes 1861–1865*, New Haven: Yale University Press, 1938.

[35] Stampp, K., *The Peculiar Institution*, N.Y.: Alfred A. Knopf, 1961.

[36] Robins, L. N., Bates, W. M., and O'Neal, P., "Adult Drinking Patterns of Former Problem Children," Ch. 23 in Pittman and Snyder, *op. cit.*

[37] Bahn, A. K., and Chandler, C. A., "Alcoholism in Psychiatric Clinic Patients," *Quart. J. Stud. Alc.* 22:411–417, 1961.

[38] Bailey, M. B., Haberman, P. W., and Alksne, H., "The Epidemiology of Alcoholism in an Urban Residential Area," *Quart. J. Stud. Alc.* 26:19–40, 1965.

[39] Bevis, W. M., "Psychological Traits of the Southern Negro with Observations as to Some of His Psychoses," *Amer. J. Psychiat.* 78:69–78, 1921.

[40] Faris, R. E. L., and Dunham, H. W., *Mental Disorders in Urban Areas*, Ch. 6, "Concentration of Alcoholic Psychoses," Chicago: University of Chicago Press, 1939.

[41] Fraenkel, M., "Hospitalized Patients with Alcohol Poisoning," *Quart. J. Stud. Alc.* 1:246–250, 1940.

[42] Garvin, W. C., "Post Prohibition Alcoholic Psychoses in New York State," *Amer. J. Psychiat.* 86:739–754, 1930.

[43] Hyde, R. W., and Chisholm, R. M., "Studies in Medical Sociology." III. "The Relation of Mental Disorders to Race and Nationality," *New Engl. J. Med.* 231:612–618, 1944.

[44] Jellinek, E. M., and Keller, M., "Rates of Alcoholism in the U. S. A., 1940–48," *Quart. J. Stud. Alc.* 13:49–59, 1952.

[45] Kirshbaum, J. D. and Shure, N., "Alcoholic Cirrhosis of the Liver. A Clinical and Pathologic Study of 356 Fatal Cases Selected from 12,267 Necropsies," *J. Lab. Clin. Med.* 28:721–731, 1943.

[46] Landis, C., and Page, J. D., *Modern Society and Mental Disease*, N. Y.: Farrar & Reinhart, 1938.

[47] Lipscomb, W. R., "Mortality Among Treated Alcoholics, A Three-Year Follow Up Study," *Quart. J. Stud. Alc.* 20:596–603, 1959.

[48] Locke, B. Z., and Duvall, H. J., "Alcoholism Among First Admissions to Ohio Public Mental Hospitals," *Quart. J. Stud. Alc.* 25:521–534, 1964.

[49] Locke, B. Z., and Duvall, H. J., "Alcoholism Among Admissions to Psychiatric Facilities," *Quart. J. Stud. Alc.* 26:303, 1965.

[50] Locke, B. Z., Kramer, M., and Pasamanick, B., "Alcoholic Psychoses Among First Admissions to Public Mental Hospitals in Ohio," *Quart. J. Stud. Alc.* 21:457–474, 1960.

[51] Malzberg, B., "Mental Diseases among Negroes in New York State," *Hum. Biol.* 7:471–513, 1935.

[52] Malzberg, B., "Migration and Mental Disease in Negroes," *Amer. J. Phys. Anthrop.* 21:107–113, 1936.

[53] Malzberg, B., "Statistics of Alcoholic Mental Disease," *Rel. Educ.* 39:22–30, 1944.

[54] Malzberg, B., "Use of Alcohol Among White and Negro Mental Patients, Comparative Statistics of First Admissions to New York State Hospitals for Mental Disease, 1939–41," *Quart. J. Stud. Alc.* 16:668–74, 1955.

[55] Malzberg, B., *The Alcoholic Psychoses, Demographic Aspect at Midcentury in New York State*, New Haven: Yale Center of Alcohol Studies, 1960.

[56] Metropolitan Life Insurance Company, "Decline in Mortality from Alcoholism," *Statistical Bull. Metrop. Life Insur. Co.* 33 (No. 3): 5–7, 1952.

[57] Moon, L. E., and Patton, R. E., "The Alcoholic Psychotic in the New York State Mental Hospitals, 1951–1960," *Quart. J. Stud. Alc.* 24:664–681, 1963.

[58] Moore, M., and Gray, M. G., "Alcoholism at Boston City Hospital. Conditions on Hospitalization of All Alcoholic Patients at the Haymarket Square Relief Station, 1923–1938," *New Engl. J. Med.* 221:49–52, 1939.

[59] Pollack, H. M., "Thirty Years of Alcoholic Mental Disease in New York State," *Psychiat. Quart.* 14:750–769, 1940.

[60] Rosanoff, A. J., *Manual of Psychiatry*, Ch. 14, "Alcoholism," New York: John Wiley & Sons, 1938.

[61] Rowntree, L. G., McGill, K. H., and Hellman, L. P., "Mental and Personality Disorders in Selective Service Registrants," *J. Amer. Med. Assn.* 128:1084–1087, 1945.

[62] Straus, R., and McCarthy, R. G., "Nonaddictive Pathological Drinking Patterns of Homeless Men," *Quart. J. Stud. Alc.* 12:601–611, 1951.

[63] Strayer, R., "A Study of the Negro Alcoholic," *Quart. J. Stud. Alc.* 22:111–123, 1961.

[64] Wagner, P., "A Comparative Study of Negro-White Admissions to the Psychiatric Pavillion of Cincinnati General Hospital," *Amer. J. Psychiat.* 95:167–183, 1938.

[65] Blacker, E., Demone, H. W., Jr., and Freeman, H. E., "Drinking Behavior of Delinquent Boys," *Quart. J. Stud. Alc.* 26:223–237, 1965.

[66] Warkov, S., Bacon, S., and Hawkins, A., "Social Correlates of Industrial Problem Drinking," *Quart. J. Stud. Alc.* 26:58–71, 1965.

[67] However Warkov, Bacon, and Hawkins (Note 66) explain their finding that Negro employees are over-represented among the identified problem drinkers as due to a higher identification risk by virtue of low educational and occupational status. Since these variables are uncontrolled, we do not know whether lower status whites exhibit the same characteristic in this particular industry or whether the problem drinking is attributable to subcultural drinking patterns of Negroes who also happen to be of low educational and occupational status.

[68] Keller, M., "The Definition of Alcoholism and the Estimation of Its Prevalence," Ch. 17 in Pittman and Snyder, *op. cit.*

[69] Wheeler, S., "Criminal Statistics: A Reformulation of the Problem," paper read at the meetings of the American Statistical Association, Philadelphia, September, 1965.

[70] Skolnick, J. H., "A Study of the Relations of Ethnic Background to Arrests for Inebriety," *Quart. J. Stud. Alc.* 15:622–630, 1954.

[71] Lightfoot, R. M., *Negro Crime In A Small Urban Community*, University of Virginia, 1934.

[72] Rochester Bureau of Municipal Research, Inc., *Man on the Periphery, A Study of the Monroe Co. (N. Y.) Penitentiary*, 1964.

[73] Scott, W. W., "An Analysis of Arrested Inebriates in Two Wisconsin Counties," *Sociol. Soc. Res.* 39:96–102, 1954.

[74] Toland, J. I., Jr., *A Comparison of (1) the Extent of Group Membership of White and Negro Men Sentenced to the District of Columbia Workhouse for Intoxication and (2) Certain Characteristics*

of the Groups to Which These Men Belong, M. A. Thesis, College Park, Maryland: University of Maryland, 1958.

[75] Zax, M., Gardner, E. A., and Hart, W. T., "Public Intoxication in Rochester, A Survey of Individuals Charged During 1961," *Quart. J. Stud. Alc.* 25:669–678, 1964.

[76] *Uniform Crime Reports*, Federal Bureau of Investigation, U. S. Department of Justice, Annual Reports for 1958–1964 (published 1959–1965).

[77] *1960 Census of Population*, Vol. I, Characteristics of the Population, Part I, U.S. Summary, U.S. Department of Commerce, Bureau of the Census.

[78] Feeney, F. E., Mindlin, D. F., Minear, V. H., and Short, E., "The Challenge of the Skid Row Alcoholic," *Quart. J. Stud. Alc.* 16:645–667, 1955.

[79] Pace, R. E., "Public Drunkenness—A Revealing Study of One City's Problem," *North Carolina Inventory*, Vol. 1–3: 14–18, 1953–1954.

[80] Wattenberg, W. W., and Moir, J. B., "A Study of Teen-Agers Arrested for Drunkenness," *Quart. J. Stud. Alc.* 17:426–436, 1956.

[81] Short, J. F., Tennyson, R. A., and Howard, K. I., "Behavior Dimensions of Gang Delinquency," *Amer. Sociol. Rev.* 28:411–428, 1963.

[82] Wilson, J. M., *Drug Addicts and Alcoholic Offenders, Negro and White: A Comparison of Social Isolation As Revealed by Certain Measurements of Social Background Factors of Subjects Incarcerated within the Correctional Institutions of the District of Columbia*, Master's Thesis, College Park, Md.: University of Maryland, 1958.

[83] Wolfgang, M. E., and Strohm, R. B., "The Relationship Between Alcohol and Criminal Homicide," *Quart. J. Stud. Alc.* 17:411–425, 1956.

[84] Roebuck, J., and Johnson, R., "The Negro Drinker and Assaulter as a Criminal Type," *Crime and Delinqu.* 8:21–33, 1962.

[85] Koren, J., *Economic Aspects of the Liquor Problem*, N.Y.: Houghton Mifflin Company, 1899. See Ch. VI, "Relations of the Negroes to the Liquor Problem."

[86] Winston and Butler's (Note 87) study of Negro bootleggers in North Carolina forty years later points to a cultural continuity here. Bootlegging is sustained both by the folkways and by the limitations of socio-economic opportunity in the area involved.

[87] Winston, S., and Butler, M., "Negro Bootleggers in Eastern North Carolina," *Am. Soc. Rev.* 8:692–697, 1943.

[88] Keller, M., "Alcoholism: Nature and Extent of the Problem," *Ann. Amer. Acad. Pol. Soc. Sci.* 315:1–11, 1958.

[89] Davis, A., and Dollard, J., *Children of Bondage: The Personality Development of Negro Youth in the Urban South*, Washington, D.C.: American Council on Education, 1940.

[90] Davis, A., Gardner, B., and Gardner, M., *Deep South, A Social Anthropological Study of Caste and Class*, Chicago: University of Chicago Press, 1941.

[91] Dollard, J., *Caste and Class in a Southern Town*, New Haven: Yale University Press, 1937.

[92] Drake, St. C., and Cayton, H., *Black Metropolis: A Study of Negro Life in a Northern City*, Vol. II, Rev. Ed., N.Y.: Harper & Row, 1962.

[93] Powdermaker, H., *After Freedom, A Cultural Study in the Deep South*, N.Y.: The Viking Press, 1939.

94 Johnson, C., *Growing Up in the Black Belt*, Washington, D.C.: American Council on Education, 1941.

95 Johnson, C., *Shadow of the Plantation*, Chicago: University of Chicago Press, 1934.

96 Myrdal, G., *An American Dilemma*, N.Y.: Harper & Row, 1964.

97 Frazier, E. F., *Black Bourgeoisie*, Glencoe, Ill.: The Free Press, 1957.

98 Bauer, R. A., "The Negro Revolution and the Negro Market," *Public Opin. Quart.*, Winter 1964, pp. 647–648.

99 Hill, M., *All-Negro Societies in Oklahoma*, Doctoral Dissertation, Chicago: University of Chicago, 1946.

100 Although Lewis (Note 101) makes social status distinctions, much of what is said about drinking in general is clearly from the vantage point of the lower status male, whose public drinking behavior must have been most accessible to him as a participant observer. Relatively little information is provided about drinking behavior of upper status "respectables," age differentials in drinking behavior, socialization to alcohol use, or the drinking behavior of lower status females.

101 Lewis, H., *Blackways of Kent*, Chapel Hill: University of North Carolina Press, 1955.

102 Morland, J. K., *Millways of Kent*, Chapel Hill: University of North Carolina Press, 1958.

103 Ashmore, H. S., *The Other Side of Jordan*, N.Y.: W. W. Norton & Company, Inc., 1960.

104 Baldwin, J., *Nobody Knows My Name*, N.Y.: The Dial Press, 1961.

105 Straus, S., and Winterbottom, M., "Drinking Patterns of an Occupational Group: Domestic Servants," *Quart. J. Stud. Alc.* 10:441–460, 1949.

106 Miller, W., *The Cool World*, N.Y.: Fawcett World Library, 1959.

107 Butcher, M. J., *The Negro in American Culture*, N.Y.: Alfred A. Knopf, 1956.

108 Maddox, G., and Allen, B., "A Comparative Study of Social Definitions of Alcohol and Its Uses among Selected Male Negro and White Undergraduates," *Quart. J. Stud. Alc.* 22:418–427, 1961.

109 Maddox, G., and Borinski, E., "Drinking Behavior of Negro Collegians: A Study of Selected Men," *Quart. J. Stud. Alc.* 25:651–668, 1964.

110 McReynolds, M., *A Comparative Study of the White and Negro High School Students' Use of Alcohol in Two Mississippi Communities*, Master's Thesis, State College: Mississippi State University, 1964.

111 Sills, J. F., *Alcohol Education: Assessment of Selected Characteristics of Negro Secondary School Students as a Basis for the Development of an Alcohol Education Program*, Doctoral Dissertation, Chapel Hill: University of North Carolina, 1963.

112 Sterne, M. W., "Drinking Among Lower Class Negro Adolescents in a Midwestern Urban Center," unpublished paper, Washington University, St. Louis: Social Science Institute, 1966.

113 Roughly 1300 of these students were urban. The remainder are described as attending a "rural" school, yet the county in which it is located is highly urbanized and is not reflective of more rural areas. Therefore our discussion has been limited to the urban sample.

114 Knupfer, G., and Room, R., "Age, Sex, and Social Class as

Factors in Amount of Drinking in a Metropolitan Community," *Social Problems* 12:224–240, 1964.

[115] Maddox, G., "Teenage Drinking in the United States," Ch. 12 in Pittman and Snyder, *op. cit.*

[116] Division of Educational Research, Purdue University, Lafayette, Ind., *The Purdue Opinion Poll for Young People*, 8:17–18, 1949.

[117] Rainwater, L., "Work and Identity in the Lower Class," in S. H. Warner, Jr., *Planning for the Quality of Urban Life*, Cambridge, Mass., forthcoming.

[118] Maddox, G., and Jennings, A., "An Analysis of Fantasy: An Exploratory Study of Social Definitions of Alcohol and Its Use by Means of A Projective Technique," *Quart. J. Stud. Alc.* 20:334–345, 1959.

[119] Since Maddox and Borinski have used the Mulford and Miller Quantity-Frequency Index discussed earlier, the same criticism with respect to the tendency of this instrument to obscure differences in quantity consumed in a given drinking episode also applies here.

[120] Mulford, H. A., and Miller, D. E., "Drinking in Iowa. IV, Preoccupation with Alcohol and Definitions of Alcohol, Heavy Drinking and Trouble Due to Drinking," *Quart. J. Stud. Alc.* 21:279–291, 1960.

[121] Mulford, H. A., and Miller, D. E., "Drinking in Iowa. III, A Scale of Definitions of Alcohol Related to Drinking Behavior," *Quart. J. Stud. Alc.* 21:267–278, 1960.

[122] Lewis points out that personal violence is part of the larger southern regional pattern and "there is a question as to how much is related primarily to—or aggravated by—the Negro's status" (Note 101, p. 211). Elsewhere he remarks that much of the drinking is also paralleled by whites in the studied community, and is not unique to the Negro community. However, Morland's (Note 102) description of lower status whites in Kent reveals that the church's position is much more explicitly condemnatory of drinking than the Negro church, that comparatively few lower status white females drink, and that there is no social drinking in the home.

7. The Chronic Drunkenness Offender
David J. Pittman
C. Wayne Gordon

[1] Strauss, R., and McCarthy, R. G., "Nonaddictive Pathological Drinking Patterns of Homeless Men," *Quart. J. Stud. Alc.*, 12:601–611, 1951.

8. Social Policy as Deviancy Reinforcement: The Case of the Public Intoxication Offender
David J. Pittman
Duff G. Gillespie

[1] Kitsuse, John I., "Societal Reaction to Deviant Behavior," *Social Problems*, 9:257–264, 1962, p. 248.

[2] Benedict, Ruth Fulton, "Anthropology and the Abnormal," in Haring, Douglas G., *Personal Character and Cultural Milieu*, Syracuse: Syracuse University Press, 1949, p. 180.

[3] Matza, David, *Delinquency and Drift*, New York: John Wiley & Sons, 1964, pp. 162–163.

[4] Schur, Edwin M., *Crimes Without Victims*, Englewood Cliffs, N.J.: Prentice Hall, 1965, p. 5.

[5] Lemert, Edwin M., *Social Pathology*, New York: McGraw-Hill, 1951, p. 76.

[6] During the summer of 1965, the authors conducted a pilot study dealing with the effect social policy had on drug addiction in metropolitan London.

[7] Dewitt Easter v. District of Columbia, Appeal from Court of General Sessions Criminal Division: Reply Brief for Appellant, Peter B. Hutt and Michael S. Horne, Covington & Burling, 701 Union Trust Building, Washington, D.C., February 6, 1965, p. 4.

[8] Joe B. Driver v. Captain Arthur Hinnant, Petition for a Writ of Habeas Corpus: Brief of American Civil Liberties Union, National Capital Area Civil Liberties Union, and Washington Area Council on Alcoholism, as *Amici Curiae*. Peter B. Hutt, and Michael S. Horne, Covington & Burling, 701 Union Trust Bldg., Washington, D.C.

[9] *Uniform Crime Reports for the United States*, Washington: U.S. Dept. of Justice, 1964, p. 112.

[10] Personal Communication: Mr. R. R. Wippel, Portland, Oregon.

[11] Benz, Elizabeth, *Man on the Periphery*, Rochester, N.Y.: Rochester Bureau of Municipal Research Inc., 1964, p. 49.

[12] Pittman, David J., and Gordon, C. W., *Revolving Door: A Study of the Chronic Police Case Inebriate*, Glencoe, Ill.: The Free Press; and New Brunswick, N.J.: Rutgers Center of Alcohol Studies, 1958.

[13] "Queries and Minor Notes: Alcoholism as a Medical Illness," *J. Amer. Med. Assn.*, 164:506, 1957.

[14] Gillespie, Duff G., "A Critical Evaluation of Alcoholism Follow-up Studies," presented at Fifteenth Annual Meeting of the Society for the Study of Social Problems, Chicago, August 28–29, 1965.

[15] Jackson, Joan K., Fagan, Ronald J., and Burr, Roscoe C., "Seattle Police Department Rehabilitation Project for Chronic Alcoholics," *Federal Probation*, 22:36–41, 1958.

9. The Legal Control of Alcoholism: Towards a Public Health
Concept
Peter Barton Hutt

[1] 19 *Corpus Juris* at 797 (1920).

[2] 4 Jac. 1, C. 5 (1606).

[3] 49 N. H. 399 (1869).

[4] Hall, *Intoxication and Criminal Responsibility*, 57 Harv. L. Rev. 1045 (1944).

[5] *M'Naghten's Case*, 10 Cl. & F. 200, 8 Eng. Rep. 718 (1843).

[6] *Flanigan* v. *People,* 86 N.Y. 554 (1881).

[7] *State* v. *Potts,* 100 N. C. 457, 6 S.E. 657 (1888).

[8] *United States* v. *Drew,* 25 Fed. Cas. No. 14,993 (C.C.D. Mass. 1828).

[9] *Choice* v. *State,* 31 Ga. 424 (1860).

[10] 209 A. 2d 625 (D.C. Ct. App. 1965) *rev'd en banc,* .... F. 2d .... (D.C. Cir. No. 19365, March 31, 1966).

[11] 243 F. Supp. 95 (E.D.N.C. 1965) *rev'd* 356 F. 2d 761 (4th Cir. 1966).

[12] Hale, *Pleas of the Crown,* Ch. IV (Circa 1675).

10. The Open Door: Sociology in an Alcoholism Treatment Facility
David J. Pittman

[1] The results of this study were published in Pittman and Gordon, *Revolving Door: A Study of the Chronic Police Case Inebriate* (Note 2).

[2] Pittman, David J., and Gordon, C. Wayne, *Revolving Door: A Study of the Chronic Police Case Inebriate,* New Brunswick, N.J.: Rutgers Center of Alcohol Studies, 1958.

[3] Pittman, David J., and Snyder, Charles R. (eds.), *Society, Culture, and Drinking Patterns,* New York: John Wiley & Sons, Inc., 1962.

[4] These impressions of the ineffectiveness of traditional health and welfare service to cope with the problem of alcoholism later were documented in an intensive field study in St. Louis. See Pittman and Sterne, *Alcoholism: Community Agency Attitudes and Their Impact on Treatment Services* (Note 5), and Sterne and Pittman, "Concept of Motivation: A Source of Institutional and Professional Blockage in the Treatment of Alcoholics" (Note 6).

[5] Pittman, David J., and Sterne, Muriel W., *Alcoholism: Community Agency Attitudes and Their Impact on Treatment Services,* Washington, D.C.: U.S. Department of Health, Education, and Welfare, Public Health Service Publication No. 1273, 1965.

[6] Sterne, Muriel W., and Pittman, David J., "The Concept of Motivation: A Source of Institutional and Professional Blockage in the Treatment of Alcoholics," *Quart. J. Stud. Alc.,* 26:41–57, March, 1965.

[7] Bliss Hospital, as many public facilities serving the indigent in American society, was constructed and provided with the barest amenities. It has always been necessary to solicit private organizations for such furnishings as draperies, record players, televisions, rugs, etc. St. Louis climate is classified by the British Diplomatic Service as being semitropical, thus the necessity for air conditioning.

[8] This point has always been difficult for some professionals to understand—particularly those who view alcoholism as the symptom of an underlying psychiatric disorder. As a sociologist, the crucial point is the person's perception of his condition. Rightly or wrongly, most alcoholics view their disorder in terms of drinking, not emotional problems. They do not view themselves as being mentally ill and resent being placed in mental institutions. The success of Alcoholics Anonymous, in part, derives from its concentration upon alcoholism as a clinical entity, regardless of the scientific dubiousness of the position.

⁹ The *St. Louis Globe Democrat,* especially M. Shepard, had extensive coverage of the alcoholism problem; for example, my appointment to the Washington University faculty was the subject of a feature story in October, 1958; Marty Mann's visit to St. Louis, in November, 1958; information articles on alcoholism and the efforts to create a public facility for alcoholics.

¹⁰ Even in 1965, Missouri remains one of the few states without a viable state program on alcoholism and St. Louis the only major city without a voluntary agency active in this field. Previous abortive attempts to form a St. Louis Council on Alcoholism are reported in Pittman and Sterne, *The Carousel: Hospitals, Social Agencies, and the Alcoholic* (Note 11).

¹¹ Pittman, David J., and Sterne, Muriel W., *The Carousel: Hospitals, Social Agencies, and the Alcoholic,* Report presented to the Missouri Division of Health, 1962.

¹² Our original estimate of a total cost of $64,000 proved too low as we also needed funds for equipping the unit. The final cost estimate was projected as being $90,000, of which we planned to secure matching funds under the Hill-Burton Hospital Construction Act. Thus, our final fund drive total was $45,000. By the fall of 1959, pledges from around one hundred business and industrial firms and labor unions for over $40,000 had been received; further pledges from over 200 individuals swelled the total to $46,153. A Hill-Burton grant of $47,500 was awarded to Bliss for the alcoholism center's construction. Thus, over $93,000 was available for constructing and equipping the alcoholism unit.

¹³ This study was supported by funds available under the National Mental Health Act to the Missouri Division of Health (H. M. Hardwicke, M.D., Acting Director), from July 1, 1959–July 30, 1962, and completed by support (in part) from a Mental Health Project Grant (MH-657) from the National Institute of Mental Health, United States Public Health Service.

¹⁴ Sterne, Muriel W., and Pittman, David J., "Teen-agers, Drinking, and the Law: A Study of Arrest Trends for Alcohol-Related Offenses," *Crime and Delinquency,* 11:78–85, 1965.

¹⁵ Sterne, Muriel W., Pittman, David J., and Coe, Thomas, "The Value to Missouri of Uniform and Centralized Crime Reporting," *Missouri Police Journal,* Autumn, 1963, pp. 15–17.

¹⁶ The findings of this survey are reported in detail elsewhere. The report presented to the Missouri Division of Health is Pittman and Sterne, *The Carousel: Hospitals, Social Agencies, and the Alcoholic* (Note 11); an abridged version is published as Pittman and Sterne, *Alcoholism: Community Agency Attitudes and Their Impact on Treatment Services* (Note 5). Other findings are published in following: Sterne and Pittman, "Teen-agers, Drinking, and the Law" (Note 14); Sterne, Pittman, and Coe, "The Value to Missouri of Uniform and Centralized Crime Reporting" (Note 15); Sterne and Pittman, "The Concept of Motivation: A Source of Institutional and Professional Blockage in the Treatment of Alcoholics" (Note 6).

¹⁷ This application entitled, "Alcoholism Treatment and Referral Demonstration Project" (MH-657), was awarded for an original period of three years (Dec. 1, 1961–Nov. 30, 1964), and was extended for

two more years (Dec. 1, 1964–Nov. 30, 1966) by the United States Public Health Service. The Principal Investigator for both periods was D. J. Pittman. Thus, funds were awarded for the demonstration project before the actual opening of the unit to patients.

[18] This assumption appears to have been justified in that the length of stay in the acute treatment room has averaged 1.7 days; it is common to find these same patients in group meetings on the third day after admission.

[19] I also am deeply indebted to other professionals who shared the milieutherapy approach and helped to establish this program at Bliss, namely, our first psychiatric residents, Ronald Catanzaro, M.D., Edwin Wolfgram, M.D., and Donald Seidel, M.D.; the Chief Psychiatric Social Worker for the Project, Laura Root, M.S.W., and an exchange social worker from The Netherlands, Johanna Bilsen; the total nursing staff at Malcolm Bliss, especially Vonceal Poiner, R.N., and Jeanne Baker, R.N.; the psychiatric aids; the custodial staff; the patients; and my fellow sociologists, particularly Muriel W. Sterne, M.A.

[20] Pittman, David J., "The Role of Sociology in the Planning and Operation of Alcoholism Programmes," *British Journal of Addiction*, 59:35–39, 1963.

[21] Gouldner, Alvin W., *Patterns of Industrial Bureaucracy*, New York: The Free Press of Glencoe, 1954.

[22] At this writing in 1966, all wards are locked except for the A.T.R.C.

[23] In 1963 my role in the A.T.R.C. had to be reduced to a 10 per cent time endeavor when I accepted the directorship of the University's Social Science Institute; in 1964 the Institute assumed full rsponsibility for the research demonstration project, and the A.T.R.C. now remains a major field site.

[24] These problems are not unique in my case. The question of the differentiation of administrative responsibilities in a hospital between hospital administrators (nonphysicians) and the medical staff is fraught with difficulty in many situations.

11. Social Therapies in the Treatment of Alcoholics
Laura Esther Root

[1] Pittman, David J., and Gordon, C. Wayne: *Revolving Door: A Study of the Chronic Police Case Inebriate*, Glencoe, Illinois: The Free Press, 1958.

[2] Jellinek, E. M.: *The Disease Concept of Alcoholism*, New Haven, Connecticut: Hillhouse Press, Yale Center of Alcoholism Studies, 1960.

[3] Jones, Maxwell: *Social Psychiatry: A Study of Therapeutic Communities*, London: Tavistock Publications, 1952.

[4] *Alcohol and the Human Body*, 16 mm. sound film, 15 minutes, Encyclopedia Britannica Films, Inc., Wilmette, Illinois, 1949.

[5] *David: Profile of a Problem Drinker*, 16 mm. sound film, 30 minutes, Producer: National Film Board of Canada, Distributed in U.S. by McGraw-Hill, 1957.

⁶ *To Your Health*, 16 mm. sound film, color, 10 minutes, Columbia University Communications Center, New York City, N.Y., 1956.

⁷ *Case #258*, 16 mm. sound film, black and white, The Loretta Young Show, National Broadcasting Company, National Council on Alcoholism, N. Y.

⁸ *Out of Orbit*, 16 mm. sound film, 14 minutes, Michigan State Board of Alcoholism, 230 North Grand Avenue, Lansing, Michigan.

⁹ *Challenge*, 16 mm. sound film, 30 minutes, Florida Alcoholic Rehabilitation Program, Avon Park, Florida.

12. The Fate of Alcoholics: An Evaluation of Alcoholism Follow-Up Studies
Duff G. Gillespie

¹ Lemere, F., "What Happens to Alcoholics," *Amer. J. Psychiat.*, 109:674–676, 1953.

² Saenger, Gerhart, and Gerard, Donald, "A Follow-Up of Patients Seen in Out-Patient Clinics Associated with the North American Association of Alcoholism Programs," presented at the Annual Meeting of the NAAAP, October 30, 1963.

³ Davies, D. L., "Normal Drinking in Recovered Alcohol Addicts," *Quart. J. Stud. Alc.*, 23:94–104, 1962.

⁴ Northcutt, T. J., "Treatment Outcome: A Follow-Up Study," Selected Papers, *North American Association of Alcoholism Programs*, pp. 23–31, 1961.

⁵ Pfeffer, H., and Berger, S., "A Follow-Up Study of Treated Alcoholics," *Quart. J. Stud. Alc.*, 18:624–648, 1957.

⁶ Wolff, Sulammith, and Holland, Lydia, "A Questionnaire Follow-Up of Alcoholic Patients," *Quart. J. Stud. Alc.*, 25:108–119, 1964.

⁷ Guze, S. B., Tuason, V. B., Stewart, M. A., and Picken, B., "The Drinking History: A Comparison of Reports by Subjects and Their Relatives," *Quart. J. Stud. Alc.*, 24:249–260, 1963.

⁸ Lipscomb, W. R., "Mortality Among Treated Alcoholics, A Three-Year Follow-Up Study," *Quart J. Stud. Alc.*, 20:596–603, 1959.

⁹ Norvig, T., and Nielsen, B., "A Follow-up Study of 221 Alcohol Addicts in Denmark," *Quart. J. Stud. Alc.*, 17:633–642, 1956.

¹⁰ Wallerstein, R. S., "Comparative Study of Treatment Methods for Chronic Alcoholism: The Alcoholism Research Project at Winter V.A. Hospital," *Amer. J. Psychiat.*, 113:228–233, 1956.

¹¹ Cowen, John, "A Six-Year Follow-Up of a Series of Committed Alcoholics," *Quart. J. Stud. Alc.*, 15:413–423, 1954.

¹² Hoff, E. C., and McKeown, C. E., "An Evaluation of the Use of Tetralthylthiuran Disulfied in the Treatment of 560 Cases of Alcohol Addiction," *Amer. J. Psychiat.*, 109:670–673, 1953.

¹³ Prout, C. T., Strongin, E. J., White, M. A., "A Study of Results in Hospital Treatment of Alcoholism in Males," *Amer. J. Psychiat.*, 107:14–19, 1950.

¹⁴ Wall, J. H., and Allen, E. B., "Results of Hospital Treatment of Alcoholism," *Amer. J. Psychiat.*, 100:474–479, 1944.

[15] Gerard, D. L., and Saenger, G., "Interval Between Intake and Follow-up as a Factor in the Evaluation of Patients with a Drinking Problem," *Quart. J. Stud. Alc.*, 20:620–630, 1959.

[16] Moore, R. A., and Ramseur, F., "Effects of Psychotherapy in an Open-Ward Hospital on Patients with Alcoholism," *Quart. J. Stud. Alc.*, 21:233–252, 1960.

[17] Davies, D. L., Shepherd, M., and Myers, E., "The Two-Year's Prognosis of 50 Alcohol Addicts After Treatment in Hospital," *Quart. J. Stud. Alc.*, 17:485–502, 1956.

[18] Mindlin, D. F., "Evaluation of Therapy for Alcoholics in a Workhouse Setting," *Quart. J. Stud. Alc.*, 21:90–112, 1960.

[19] Bruun, Kettil, "Outcome of Different Types of Treatment of Alcoholics," *Quart. J. Stud. Alc.* 24:280–288, 1963.

13. Measures of Treatment Outcome for Alcoholics: A Model of Analysis
Sarah Lee Boggs

[1] Mindlin, D. F., "The Characteristics of Alcoholics as Related to Prediction of Treatment Outcome," *Quart. J. Stud. Alc.*, 20:604–619, 1959.

[2] Gibbins, R. J., and Armstrong, J. D., "Effects of Clinical Treatment on Behavior of Alcoholic Patients," *Quart. J. Stud. Alc.*, 18:429–450, 1957.

[3] Williams, J. H., *Florida Project on Vocational Rehabilitation of Treated Alcoholics*, Avon Park, Fla.: State of Florida Alcoholic Rehabilitation Program, 1964, pp. 24–40.

[4] Hagood, M. J., and Price, D. O., *Statistics for Sociologists*, New York: Holt, Rinehart and Winston, 1952, Chapter 10.

[5] Pfeffer, A. Z., and Berger, S., "A Follow-Up Study of Treated Alcoholics," *Quart. J. Stud. Alc.*, 18:624–648, 1957.

[6] Selzer, M. L., and Holloway, W. H., "A Follow-Up of Alcoholics Committed to a State Hospital," *Quart. J. Stud. Alc.*, 18:98–120, 1957.

[7] Moore, R. A., and Ramseur, F., "Effects of Psychotherapy in an Open-Ward Hospital on Patients with Alcoholism," *Quart. J. Stud. Alc.*, 21:233–252, 1960.

[8] Davies, D. L., Shepherd, M., and Myers, E., "The Two-Years' Prognosis of 50 Alcohol Addicts After Treatment in Hospital," *Quart. J. Stud. Alc.*, 17:485–502, 1956.

[9] Pittman, D. J., and Sterne, M. W., *Alcoholism: Community Agency Attitudes and Their Impact on Treatment Services*, Washington: Public Health Service publication No. 1273, 1963.

[10] Hollingshead, A. B. and Redlich, F. C., *Social Class and Mental Illness*, New York: John Wiley & Sons, Inc., 1958.

[11] Pittman, D. J., "The Role of Sociology in the Planning and Operation of Alcoholism Treatment Programmes," *The British Journal of Addiction*, January, 1963, pp. 35–39.

[12] Guze, S. B., Tuason, V. B., Stewart, M. A., and Picken, B.,

"The Drinking History: A Comparison of Reports by Subjects and Their Relatives," *Quart. J. Stud. Alc.*, 24:349–360, 1963.

[13] The degree of association between two variables is measured by the amount of difference that the correlation coefficient is from 1.0. A perfect correlation of 1.0 indicates that the variables are perfectly related to each other, so that changes in one variable are associated with comparable changes in the other. The direction of association can be either positive or negative.

A perfect positive rank order correlation coefficient (+ 1.0) would indicate that cases ranking the highest on the in-take drinking scale would also rank the highest on the follow-up drinking scale, and the converse. A perfect negative rank order correlation coefficient (− 1.0) would indicate that the cases ranking the highest on the in-take drinking scale would rank the lowest on the follow-up drinking scale, and the converse.

14. Analysis of Various Community Approaches to the Problem of Alcoholism in the United States
David J. Pittman
Muriel W. Sterne

[1] Shepherd, Ernest A., "Current Resources for Therapy, Education, and Research," *Ann. Amer. Acad. Pol. Soc. Sci.* 315:133–143, 1958.

15. Alcoholics Anonymous: An Interpretation
Milton A. Maxwell

[1] Maxwell, Milton A., "Factors Affecting an Alcoholic's Willingness to Seek Help," *Northwest Science,* 28:116–123, 1954.

[2] *Alcoholics Anonymous Comes of Age: A Brief History of A.A.,* New York: Alcoholics Anonymous Publishing, 1957.

[3] Maxwell, Milton A., "Interpersonal Factors in the Genesis and Treatment of Alcohol Addiction," *Social Forces,* 29:443–448, 1951. *Social Factors in the Alcoholics Anonymous Program,* unpublished doctoral dissertation, University of Texas, 1949.

[4] Tiebout, Harry M., "The Act of Surrender in the Therapeutic Process with Special Reference to Alcoholism," *Quart. J. Stud. Alc.,* 10:48–58, 1949.

[5] Tiebout, Harry M., "Surrender Versus Compliance in Therapy with Special Reference to Alcoholism," *Quart. J. Stud. Alc.,* 14:58–68, 1953.

[6] Tiebout, Harry M., "The Ego Factor in Surrender in Alcoholism," *Quart. J. Stud. Alc.,* 15:610–621, 1954.

[7] Stewart, David A., "The Dynamics of Fellowship as Illustrated in Alcoholics Anonymous," *Quart J. Stud. Alc.,* 16:251–262, 1955.

[8] Stewart, David A., *Preface to Empathy,* New York: Philosophical Library, 1956.

[9] Ripley, Herbert S., and Jackson, Joan K., "Therapeutic Factors in Alcoholics Anonymous," *Amer. J. Psychiat.*, 116:44–50, 1959.

[10] Lindt, Hendrik, "The 'Rescue' Fantasy in Group Treatment of Alcoholics," *Inter. J. of Group Psychotherapy*, 9:43–52, 1959.

[11] Lewin, Kurt, and Grabbe, Paul, "Conduct, Knowledge, and Acceptance of New Values," in Gertrud W. Lewin (ed.), *Resolving Social Conflicts*, New York: Harper & Row, 1948, pp. 56–68.

[12] Trice, Harrison M., "A Study of the Process of Affiliation with Alcoholics Anonymous," *Quart. J. Stud. Alc.*, 18:39–43, 1957.

[13] Trice, Harrison M., "The Affiliation Motive and Readiness to Join Alcoholics Anonymous," *Quart. J. Stud. Alc.*, 20:313–320, 1959.

[14] Ritchie, Oscar W., "A Sociohistorical Survey of Alcoholics Anonymous," *Quart. J. Stud. Alc.*, 9:119–156, 1955.

16. Governmental Responses to Alcoholism in North America
Augustus H. Hewlett

[1] Shepherd, Ernest A., "Official Agencies," an address delivered at the National Council on Alcoholism Annual Meeting, April 10, 1964.

[2] Plaut, Thomas F. A., "The State Alcoholism Program Movement: A Critical Analysis," from *Selected Papers* delivered at the 15th Annual Meeting of NAAAP, Portland, Oregon, September 1964, pp. 74, 79, 80.

17. No References

Index